Land Warfare: Brassey

Weapons Systems &

Volume 3

Noise in the
Military Environment

Land Warfare:
Brassey's New Battlefield Weapons Systems and Technology
Series

Executive Editor: Colonel R G Lee OBE, Former Military Director of
Studies, Royal Military College of Science,
Shrivenham, UK

Editor-in-Chief: Professor Frank Hartley, Principal and Dean, Royal
Military College of Science, Shrivenham, UK

The success of the first series on Battlefield Weapons Systems and
Technology and the pace of advances in military technology has
prompted Brassey's to produce a new Land Warfare series. This series
updates subjects covered in the original series and also covers completely new areas. The books are written for military men who wish to
advance their professional knowledge. In addition, they are intended
to aid anyone who is interested in the design, development and production of military equipment.

Volume I   Guided Weapons — R G Lee *et al*

Volume II   Explosives, Propellants and Pyrotechnics — A Baily
and S G Murray

Volume III   Noise in the Military Environment — R F Powell and
M R Forrest

Volume IV   Ammunition — P R Courtney-Green and E G Archer

For full details of titles in the series, please contact your local
Brassey's/Pergamon office.

Noise in the Military Environment

R. F. POWELL
Royal Military College of Science, Shrivenham, UK

and

M. R. FORREST
Army Personnel Research Establishment, Farnborough, UK

BRASSEY'S DEFENCE PUBLISHERS
(a member of the Maxwell Pergamon Publishing Corporation plc)

LONDON · OXFORD · WASHINGTON · NEW YORK
BEIJING · FRANKFURT · SÃO PAULO · SYDNEY · TOKYO · TORONTO

U.K. (Editorial)	Brassey's Defence Publishers Ltd., 24 Gray's Inn Road, London WC1X 8HR
(Orders)	Brassey's Defence Publishers Ltd., Headington Hill Hall, Oxford OX3 0BW, England
U.S.A. (Editorial)	Pergamon-Brassey's International Defense Publishers, Inc., 8000 Westpark Drive, Fourth Floor, McLean, Virginia 22102, U.S.A.
(Orders)	Pergamon Press, Inc., Maxwell House, Fairview Park, Elmsford, New York 10523, U.S.A.
PEOPLE'S REPUBLIC OF CHINA	Pergamon Press, Room 4037, Qianmen Hotel, Beijing, People's Republic of China
FEDERAL REPUBLIC OF GERMANY	Pergamon Press GmbH, Hammerweg 6, D-6242 Kronberg, Federal Republic of Germany
BRAZIL	Pergamon Editora Ltda, Rua Eça de Queiros, 346, CEP 04011, Paraiso, São Paulo, Brazil
AUSTRALIA	Pergamon-Brassey's Defence Publishers Pty Ltd., P.O. Box 544, Potts Point, N.S.W. 2011, Australia
JAPAN	Pergamon Press, 5th Floor, Matsuoka Central Building, 1-7-1 Nishishinjuku, Shinjuku-ku, Tokyo 160, Japan
CANADA	Pergamon Press Canada Ltd., Suite No. 271, 253 College Street, Toronto, Ontario, Canada M5T 1R5

Copyright © 1988 Brassey's Defence Publishers Ltd.

First edition 1988

Library of Congress Cataloging in Publication Data
Powell, R. F.
Noise in the military environment.
(Land warfare; v. 3)
Bibliography: p.
Includes index.
1. Armed Forces — Noise. I. Forrest, M. R.
II. Title. III. Series.
UA10.P68 1988 363.7'41 88-4330

British Library Cataloguing in Publication Data
Powell, R. F.
Noise in the military environment. —
(Brassey's land warfare series; v. 3).
1. Military equipment. Noise. Control measures
I. Title II. Forrest, M. R.   363.7'46

ISBN 0-08-035830-6 Hardcover
ISBN 0-08-035831-4 Flexicover

Cover: MLRS (Photo: Vought Corporation USA)

*Printed in Great Britain by
Richard Clay Ltd, Chichester, Sussex*

Preface

This Series
This series of books is written for those who wish to improve their knowledge of military weapons and equipment. It is equally relevant to professional soldiers, those involved in developing or producing military weapons or indeed anyone interested in the art of modern warfare.

All the texts are written in a way which assumes no mathematical knowledge and no more technical depth than would be gleaned by any person who keeps himself or herself informed of developments in the modern world. It is intended that the books should be of particular interest to officers in the Armed Services wishing to further their professional knowledge as well as anyone involved in research, development, production, testing and maintenance of defence equipments.

The principal authors of the books are all members of the staff of the Royal Military College of Science, Shrivenham, which is composed of a unique blend of academic and military experts. They are not only leaders in the technology of their subjects, but are aware of what the military practitioner needs to know. It is difficult to imagine any group of persons more fitted to write about the application of technology to the battlefield.

This Volume
There is an increasing public awareness of the problem of noise, and its effect on our living environment. It is particularly hazardous to hearing in the military environment. In spite of the known risks, noise levels from military equipment are increasing, to an extent that conventional hearing protection may be inadequate.

This book is the first to deal with noise from the military point of view and has evolved from courses run by RMCS Shrivenham. Its particular concern is to identify hearing hazards and describe the practical ways of reducing them. It is intended for all soldiers and civilians working with noisy equipment. The technical background is built up from very basic ideas using a variety of actual case histories involving vehicles, aircraft, workshops, weapons and equipments. Much of the material comes from the practical experience of the authors and has not been readily available previously.

January 1988   FRANK HARTLEY
Shrivenham   GEOFFREY LEE

Acknowledgements

The authors are grateful to the large number of individuals in the Services and Government Establishments who have co-operated in our respective noise measurement programmes over many years. RFP would particularly like to thank Don Tubby of Logistics Executive (Army) for his enthusiasm and assistance.

We would both like to thank Julie Wiltshire for so efficiently transforming two sets of handwriting onto a word-processor and Bob Steavenson for drawing the figures.

October 1987   R.F.P.
Shrivenham   M.R.F

Contents

List of Illustrations

1. Introduction

This chapter gives an overview of the problem of noise in a military environment. It traces the history of the problem, shows how the problem can be overcome, and gives an indication of the limits of our present knowledge and of possible developments in the future.

The Military Noise Problem — A History

The problem of noise in a military environment is a comparatively new one. Although there are earlier sporadic references to deafness from noise of gunfire or explosions, it was not until the FIRST WORLD WAR that the problem gained any substantial attention. This was parallelled by the attention given to noise-induced hearing loss in industry; although the incidence of noise-induced hearing loss must have been increasing since the start of the Industrial Revolution, and indeed papers on the subject appeared in the medical press during the nineteenth century, little was done to alleviate the problem.

There were a number of reasons for this inaction. The obvious one is that noise exposure was, on the whole, neither as intense nor as widespread as it is today. Other reasons are that neither noise nor hearing loss could, at the time, be measured with any accuracy; military medical standards were less stringent; expectations of health and quality of life were also much less developed than they are now.

After a flurry of medical papers on deafness from gunfire or explosions during the FIRST WORLD WAR, the subject continued to attract little attention until the Second, when it became obvious that noise exposure was a serious cause of disability. Much excellent work was done, and the basic principles were clearly established. It was shown that the hearing loss, which varied between individuals, was due to destruction of the hair (nerve) cells in the inner ear, whether from continuous or gunfire noise; maximum 'safe' limits were established, and the principles and use of hearing protection were elucidated.

After the SECOND WORLD WAR, much of this knowledge became relegated to the back numbers of learned journals. Hearing protection was rarely used; equipment was designed with little thought for noise emission. Even when limits were set for noise from gunfire, these appeared to be based chiefly on the risk of ear drum rupture, even though the hearing loss had been shown previously to be caused by damage to the inner ear.

Gradually the importance of noise became more widely recognised. This recognition in the military sphere progressed hand-in-hand with a parallel recognition of the importance of noise in industry; indeed, much of the research into noise-induced hearing loss has been prompted by industry. At the same time, research into noise was also driven by concern over noise in the environment and its effect on the quality of life. The growth in road and air transport, especially the increasing use of gas turbine engines in aviation, was largely responsible for this; they are, subjectively, much more noisy than their piston-engine predecessors, due to their greater high-frequency content.

Research on noise then enjoyed a period of expansion. It was a great age for the development of new acoustic units. The decibel was joined by the phon, the sone, the noy; complicated noise-rating schemes were developed, by far the most important (and the most long-lasting, due to their importance in planning and legislation) being related to aircraft noise nuisance. The development of subjective rating scales for loudness and annoyance was matched by a massive literature on noise-induced hearing loss, in which measurements of temporary threshold shift (TTS) played a prominent part.

More recently, a general consolidation has taken place. Most of the complicated rating schemes and their specialised units are now little used. The exception is annoyance due to aircraft noise, a topic so specialised as to be beyond the scope of this little book. The emphasis now is on units that are easily measured, elegantly defined and simple to understand. Two concepts have largely taken the place of their many predecessors — the 'A' frequency weighting and the concept of equivalent continuous noise level.

So universally used are these two concepts that there is a serious danger of considering them to provide a complete description of the ear's response. It must be emphasised that they are only convenient approximations; the ear is a complex instrument and, despite a vast amount of research, its functioning in some respects is still not fully understood.

Noise Reduction and Hearing Conservation

It is, of course, one thing to be able to describe the ear's response, even if only approximately, and quite another thing to be able to use the knowledge effectively. The practice of noise reduction and hearing conservation has, in both industrial and military environments, seriously lagged behind the available knowledge. The need in practical terms is for application of existing knowledge rather than for further research.

Some practical examples will illustrate this. Noise in fighting vehicles has tended to increase, despite greater availability of noise reduction techniques. In one modern fighting vehicle, a level of 130 dB is reached in normal operation. A similar situation exists in aircraft and in ships' engine rooms. Voice communication has therefore become more difficult, but existing communications equipment does not take full advantage of available techniques for improving communication. High noise levels are encountered, not only in operation, but also during maintenance. Part of the problem is doubtless unavoidable, but a substantial part arises from failure to consider noise at the design or procurement stages.

A series of surveys undertaken on British infantry soldiers, in 1965, 1969 and 1979, showed that slightly less than half had some degree of noise-induced hearing loss, and that the proportion hardly changed despite the introduction of hearing protection (a V-51R pattern prefabricated earplug) in 1966. A survey of hearing in the US Army in the late 1970s told the same story. Indeed the problem is universal in all national forces. The proportion of men with hearing which is too bad for continued military service is small, but by no means negligible.

The failure of the issued hearing protection to protect hearing holds some interesting lessons. The V-51R ear plug is potentially an effective device against both continuous and gunfire noise, and its efficiency had been demonstrated in numerous tests. However, it is effective only when in the ear, rather than in the pocket or on the Quartermaster's shelves; and the very necessary provision of the correct size, from a choice of five, proved an intractable problem. In theory, the correct size should have been chosen by the unit medical officer, but it was clear that this did not always happen. It was quite obvious, from casual visits to ranges, that the device was unpopular, was considered ineffective and uncomfortable, and was frequently not used. When it was used, it was often badly fitted and ineffective. What should in theory have been an effective solution failed, in practical usage, to protect the majority of those at risk. The problem was by no means confined to ear plugs. Ear muffs were often seen to be ill-used, sometimes with a beret beneath the ear cup seal so that daylight was visible between the ear seal and the head. The seals were frequently damaged.

The main lesson is that the provision of hearing protection is but one part of a hearing conservation programme; education, enforcement and monitoring audiometry are also necessary. Another lesson is that a good performance in tests carried out in ideal conditions is by itself no guarantee of good performance in practical usage. The experience from these lessons is now being put into practice. Hearing conservation measures have become more effective in recent years, although much remains to be done.

The effect of a lack of basic knowledge in military applications of acoustics is regrettably obvious in the procurement of military equipment. With a few honourable exceptions, noise is specified only in very vague terms. Often the statement follows the line that noise must be no greater than that of the item due for replacement. Even such a vague statement as this is often disregarded in development. The noise may not be considered until an advanced prototype is constructed, by which time it is too late to reduce the noise without a major re-design. This has been especially noticeable in the design of armoured vehicles. The result is either excessive noise, or a need for a expensive modification.

What of the future? The trend for more power from equipment of reduced size and weight will tend to give ever-increasing noise levels; increased concern for health and military efficiency will argue for reducing noise. The operation of a wider range of equipment, especially by infantry forces, will add to the total noise exposure. Prediction is a risky business, but it is reasonable to assume that the study and practice of acoustics, in military as in civil fields, will continue to grow in importance.

The need for active electronic solutions to reduce noise reaching the ear, and to improve the signal-to-noise ratio in communications systems, is likely to increase; but these systems are by no means a panacea, and are not a substitute for the correct use of more conventional solutions.

Increased concern over the environment and the quality of life is likely to place increased restrictions on the use of noisy equipment, especially large calibre guns and explosives, during peacetime training. This is already happening with low flying aircraft and ground engine tests on airfields.

Finally, increased knowledge of human response to noise will, in the very long term, lead to improved methods in its rating. However, there is a very long way to go before current research bears fruit.

This Book

This book has grown out of Military Noise courses run by RMCS, Shrivenham, for the British Army, RAF and associated civilian personnel. It is intended particularly for medical officers, project managers, present and future commanding officers of units using noise aircraft, vehicles or equipment, hearing conservation and safety officers, workshop supervisors and those involved in teaching safety matters.

It is not a standard textbook. It assumes no previous knowledge of acoustics and is built up using military case histories in both the text and the self test questions. There is an emphasis on areas of particular service interest, such as weapon noise, where there is no other readily available literature at this level.

Summary

The increasing noise emission from modern military equipment, coupled with greater awareness of its effects, makes the study of noise in the military environment of increasing importance. The principal need is for greater awareness of existing knowledge. Acoustical considerations are of increasing importance in the design and procurement of new equipment. Hearing conservation programmes, based on awareness of practical factors in the everyday work of service personnel, are becoming increasingly effective but much remains to be done.

2. The Characteristics of Sound

Sound Waves

Sound waves are basically pressure waves spreading out through the environment due to a disturbance produced at a source. Such sources may be vibrating panels displacing air, the turbulent mixing of gases near exhausts or the impulsive pressure variations from explosions. It is not only the pressure in the transmitting medium that is changed by the passage of the sound wave, but pressure forms the basis of most sound measurement and is worth some discussion.

Acoustic Pressure

The pressure variations due to these sources spread out in the surrounding air at the local speed of sound. Figure 2.1 shows such waves spreading out from a small source.

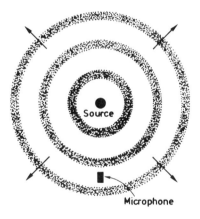

FIG. 2.1 Spherical waves from a source

If the source were a tuning fork, the microphone used to measure the pressure changes would sense them as changing regularly with time as in Figure 2.2, which is a sinusoidal wave. These acoustic pressures are superimposed on the local atmospheric pressure but are usually much smaller. The acoustic pressure averaged over time for the curve shown is zero since the compressions (pressure above atmospheric) cancel out the rarefactions (pressure below atmospheric). There is thus little to gain in merely measuring averaged acoustic pressure.

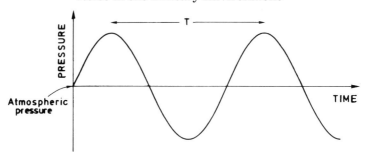

FIG. 2.2 Sinusoidal pressure wave

Sound waves, however, transmit energy and this energy depends on the square of the acoustic pressure. Squaring the pressure values of Figure 2.2 gives the p^2 curve of Figure 2.3 which no longer has an average of zero. The measuring instrument averages out this p^2 curve over time and then takes the square root of this average. This gives the 'root-mean-square' (rms) pressure written as p_{rms}. It is necessary to ensure that the time over which averaging is carried out is sufficient to prevent errors; for example, it is long enough to include many complete fluctuations of pressure. For the sine wave of Figure 2.2, p_{rms} is related to the maximum pressure p_{max} by the relation $p_{rms} = p_{max}/\sqrt{2}$.

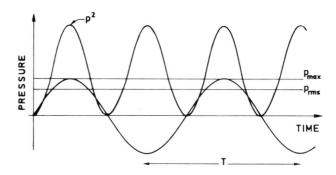

FIG. 2.3 Root-mean-square pressure

Pressures are measured in newtons per square metre (abbreviated to N m^{-2}), the newton being the unit of force. This pressure unit, termed the pascal, is very small. Normal atmospheric pressure is 100,000 (10^5) pascals.

Frequency

An important quantity in Figure 2.2 is the time elapsing between one pressure maximum and the next, i.e. the time it takes the wave to repeat itself. This is called the period (T) measured in seconds and the frequency is $1/T$, expressed in hertz (Hz). Real sounds are composed of various frequencies. The frequency content is a vital characteristic of any source since it determines how loud it seems, how damaging it might be, how we might quieten it and what is the most suitable hearing protector.

A convenient way of showing the frequency content of a sound is to plot the energy present at various frequencies against frequency to get a so-called frequency spectrum. For the pure tone this gives Figure 2.4. All the energy is concentrated at one frequency.

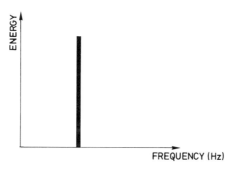

FIG. 2.4 Energy spectrum for a pure tone

Such pure tones are often accompanied by frequencies which are multiples of this lowest (fundamental) frequency. These higher frequencies are called harmonics. Figure 2.5 is a typical example.

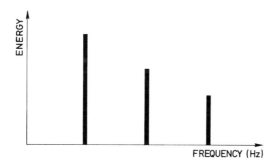

FIG. 2.5 Energy spectrum with harmonics

Random noise contains all the frequencies in a particular range, shown in Figure 2.6.

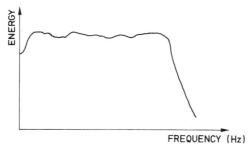

FIG. 2.6 Broad band energy spectrum

A Lynx helicopter produces sound that is a mixture of these types. Figure 2.7 shows the large peaks in its spectrum corresponding to a fundamental at 22 Hz and harmonics at 44, 66 . . . Hz due to the main rotor. There is also a peak at 122 Hz due to the tail rotor.

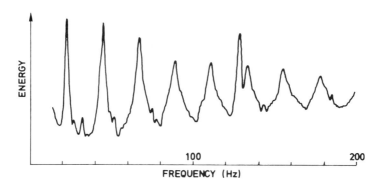

FIG. 2.7 Energy spectrum of Lynx helicopter

Figure 2.7 used measurements spaced only 0.5 Hz apart, involving 400 pieces of information for the frequency range of 200 Hz used. The wider range of frequencies involved in noise problems would involve far too much data if looked at in the same detail, and for human response to noise it is often sufficient to measure over octave intervals or bands.

Octave intervals are such that the upper frequency limit (f_2) is approximately twice the lower one (f_1). The centre frequency (f_0) is defined as:

$$f_0 = \sqrt{f_1 f_2}.$$

Commonly used centre frequencies f_0 are: 31.5, 63, 125, 250, 500, 1000, 2000, 4000, 8000 and 16000 Hz

These centre frequencies are shown in Figure 2.8 as well as the range effectively covered in each octave band. When we use an octave band at one of these centre frequencies, we thus also accept energy from frequencies on either side over a total range called the bandwidth. Here the bandwidths are 0.71 times the respective f_0. As we go up through the f_0's the bandwidth thus increases.

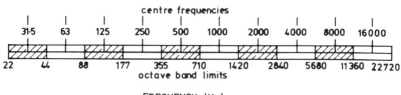

FIG. 2.8 Octave frequency bands

Figure 2.9 shows the frequency distribution in octave bands measured 1 m from a gas turbine engine during a test run. The amount of energy is plotted vertically and the frequency horizontally, both on logarithmic scales, which makes it easier to include wide ranges of values. On the vertical scale, the energy is given in decibels, a term we will define in the next chapter. The 16 kHz band has been omitted since the energy in this band was very small.

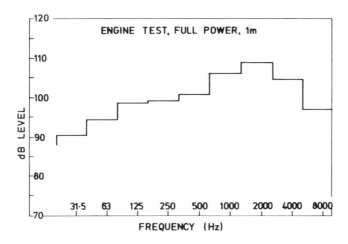

FIG. 2.9 Energy spectrum of a gas turbine engine

Wavelength

If we could photograph the pure-tone wave at a particular time as it spread out, we would get Figure 2.10 which shows how the acoustic pressure varies with distance. The variation is again regular and we define the distance over which the wave repeats itself as the wavelength, λ.

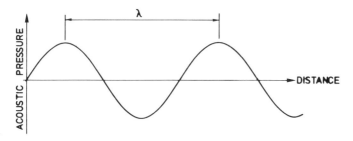

FIG. 2.10 Definition of wavelength

Wavelength, frequency and the speed of sound (v) are related by the equation:

$$v = f \lambda$$

With v in metres per second, f in Hz and λ in metres.

Wavelength is important as is reveals how much notice a wave will take of an obstacle in its path. A sharp shadow will be created only if the object is much greater in size than the wavelength. If the converse is true the wave spreads round the obstacle, by a process known as diffraction. This has obvious implications when we try to use a barrier to block sound, and for the effect of the human head on sound reaching it.

For example, to calculate the height a barrier needs to block off a sound source having a dominant frequency of 100 Hz, we must calculate the wavelength (λ). Using $v = f\lambda$, if v is 330 m s^{-1}, then λ is $v/f = 3.3$ m. The barrier must be about two wavelengths, or about 6 m, high to be effective! It must also be wide enough to prevent spreading around the sides. Trees are often used as noise screens but these are very ineffective except at higher frequencies when the wavelengths become smaller than the branches and foliage.

Reflection

Large surfaces reflect sound falling on them. At higher frequencies reflections from the human frame can have a marked effect on the sound pressure at a microphone placed close to the body. The presence of reflecting surfaces always means that the energy reaching a point in an enclosed space will be higher than in the open air.

Sound usually reaches us by several different paths. In Figure 2.11 a direct wave

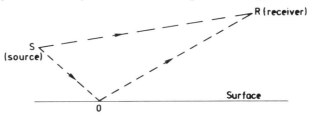

FIG. 2.11 Reflected and direct waves

from the source S to the receiver R joins one reflected at O from a nearby surface. The combination of the two may produce positions of R at which the crests are in phase (coincide) and add together, as in Figure 2.12a; at the other positions they may be out of phase and subtract (Figure 2.12b). The condition which applies depends on the difference in the distance covered by the alternative paths: they will be in-phase for a whole number of wavelengths difference and out-of-phase for odd numbers of half-wavelengths. This is called the interference effect. We are ignoring any phase changes during reflection itself. The waves must have the same frequency for interference to occur so that the effect is reduced by having many frequencies present.

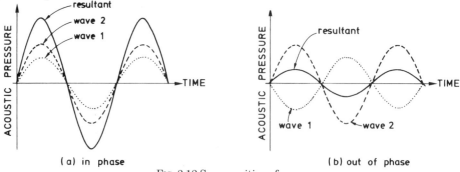

FIG. 2.12 Superposition of waves

Reflections can also give problems in measuring sound levels in room where some waves may always add at one place and always subtract at another. The effect is particularly marked in rooms of a simple shape with rigid well-reflecting walls; sound waves of a particular wavelength find that they can fit into the room dimensions just as the waves in an organ pipe fit into its length. Hi-fi enthusiasts should be well aware of the implications. There are optimum positions of a source in a room for the most efficient propagation of the sound, using the reflection from nearby walls; one such position is in a corner. This is also very relevant to workshop noise. We do not wish to propagate sound efficiently from an engine on a mainte- nance run to all parts of the workshop and so the engine should not be placed in a corner, against the usual brick or breeze block walls.

Spreading

As the energy produced at the sound source moves out into the surroundings, it usually spreads out over an ever-increasing area. If this spreading takes place equally in all directions we could visualise the source as producing spherical waves (Figure 2.1), a simple situation welcomed by text books as an omnidirectional point source. The sound pressure would be the same at a given distance all round the source. In practice most sound sources are too large to be considered as simple point sources, and the sound pressure can vary considerably around them. We come to the first problem in a noise survey: where do we measure the 'typical' sound level? This is particularly important when we wish to measure the noise close to the source, as for an operator near an engine power pack or an aircraft.

Sound Intensity

The amount of acoustic energy emitted by a source every second is called its acoustic power, expressed in watts. The power of acoustic sources covers an enorm- ous range, from several kilowatts for a jet engine on reheat to 10 W inside a noisy vehicle, 1 mW for a shouting voice and 10^{-9} W for a romantic whisper.

Positioned usually at some distance from a source, we need to know how much of the energy it emits actually reaches us. It is conventionally agreed that this should be expressed in terms of the energy crossing one square metre every second at our location. This quantity is called the sound intensity, measured in watts per square metre (abbreviated to W m^{-2}).

The point source produces waves which spread out as spheres. At a distance r from the source the energy it radiates every second is spread out over the area of a sphere, that is an area $4\pi r^2$. The intensity is thus $W/4\pi r^2$. If r is doubled, the area increases by a factor of four and the intensity is reduced by four times.

If we assume the point source law works we can easily estimate the intensities these produce at given distances. A jet engine radiating 1200 W would give an intensity 10 m away of $1200/(4\pi \times 10^2)$, i.e. about 1 W m^{-2}. The shouting voice at 1 m would produce $10^{-3}/(4\pi \times 1^2)$ or 8×10^{-5} W m^{-2}, and the romantic whisper at 1 cm range gives 8×10^{-7} W m^{-2}.

Atmospheric Transmission Effects

In addition to the reduction of intensity with distance, the atmosphere itself may also remove energy from the waves or scatter the sound. The higher frequencies are particularly affected by molecular absorption. One practical consequence of this will be discussed in Chapter 11. Air movement due to turbulence may also scatter the sound. The resulting sound intensity may well vary with time as conditions in the atmosphere itself change.

Ray bending can result from wind and temperature gradients. Winds usually increase in strength as height increases, and consequently bend the sound towards the ground downwind of the source. Upwind of the source, there would be ray bending upwards and the creation of a shadow zone due to the decreased number of rays reaching every square metre of surface (Figure 2.13).

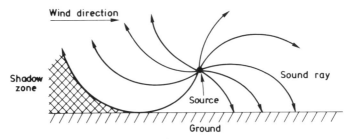

FIG. 2.13 Ray bending by wind

In the absence of wind the waves travel in straight lines until they enter obliquely a region in which the speed of sound is different. The speed of sound increases as temperature increases from 331 m s^{-1} at 0°C to 343 m s^{-1} at 20°C. An increase of temperature with height will thus result in the waves being bent (refracted) downwards (Figure 2.14). Sound intensities at distant points can then be enhanced to an unacceptable degree. Such temperature conditions, called inversions, are most common at night or early in the morning.

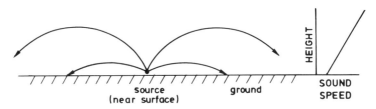

FIG. 2.14 Refraction due to temperature increase with height

On the other hand, if the temperature decreases with height, the waves will be refracted upward to create a shadow zone near the ground (Figure 2.15).

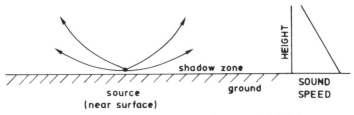

FIG. 2.15 Refraction due to temperature decrease with height

Atmospheric conditions may combine these temperature effects. In particular the presence of a minimum temperature at some height may cause focusing of sound at a distant point as rays are brought together by refraction (Figure 2.16).

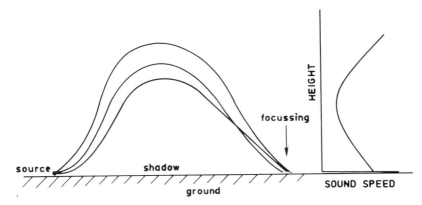

FIG. 2.16 Focusing due to temperature gradients

The resulting problem, familiar to many working on heavy weapon ranges who are concerned with local complaints, is to predict when and where such focusing is likely. The probable enhancement in sound intensity is also required. All such predictions are complicated by the rapid changes in atmospheric conditions that are all too possible. Continually updated meterological data is needed to allow equations to be used to trace the ray paths through the air and even then predictions would be unreliable. Without such data, recourse is usually made to blanket restrictions that will not permit firing if the cloud base is too low (producing too much reflection downwards), if there is a temperature inversion and/or if a surface wind is blowing towards the sensitive area. This procedure reduces complaints by severely restricting the use of the range.

Summary

This chapter has covered matters vital to the understanding of the noise problem, particularly the reasons why frequency and wavelength are important. The ability to understand and interpret frequency spectra such as Figure 2.9 is essential for a real appreciation of hearing hazard and effective hearing protection since both depend on the frequency content of the source. The amount of energy reaching the ear, expressed in terms of sound intensity, depends on the acoustic power of each source present and on the paths taken by the sound. This can be clearly seen using the example of the moving tank in Figure 2.17. There are many sound sources on such a vehicle including the track links hitting the ground, the engine itself, the exhaust system and smaller items such as cooling fans close to an ear. Energy from the sources may be transmitted through air or through the hull material itself; which source dominates depends then on the position of the receiver. The commander head-out position, for instance, may have a large contribution from the exhaust. For observers outside the tank, their position, as well as reflections or energy losses due to the terrain or the atmosphere, will determine the received sound level.

FIG. 2.17 Sound sources in a tank

Figure 2.18 shows the acoustic environment being measured close to the driver's head while the vehicle is stationary.

FIG. 2.18 Measurement of sound level at tank driver's position

We now need to discuss how such measurements of sound are expressed.

SELF TEST QUESTIONS

Question 1   A loudspeaker transmits speech in the range from 300 to 3000 Hz. Calculate the wavelengths involved if the speed of sound in air is 330 ms.

Answer ....

....

....

Question 2   Why is it difficult to heat a kettle of water by shouting at it?

Answer ....

....

....

Question 3   A helicopter on a ground run emits sound of frequency 19 Hz and 1257 Hz due to its rotors. Which of these would be easiest to reduce for local residents, using an earth bank?

Answer ....

....

....

Question 4   A sentry locates a sound by the difference in the intensity produced at his ears due to shadowing by his head. Estimate the frequency below which the method fails. (Take the speed of sound from Question 1.)

Answer ....

....

....

Question 5   What is the sound intensity 10 m from a source of spherical waves emitting 100 W?

Answer ....

....

....

Answers on page 112.

3. The Decibel and its Use

This chapter introduces the decibel system of measurement and explains its advantages. This is one of the most important sections of the book and also one of the most demanding. The reader is assured that the effort will be worth it in any attempt to understand noise.

Logarithmic Scales

In the military environment we have to deal with an enormous range of sound intensity. The intensity inside a tank can be 1,000,000,000 times greater than for rustling combat sounds. Such a range of numbers is not easy to deal with: in graphical terms it becomes impractical. For example, let us take the quiet rustle as a base value and describe the other sounds as multiples of that. Figure 3.1 shows such ratios as vertical bars on a linear vertical scale. The 10^6 bar is too small to be seen and we would have a lot of information packed together at the bottom of the scale. We need to expand this bottom section without affecting the top part. One way to do this would be to replace a multiplication by ten into an addition of one.

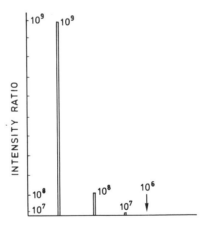

FIG. 3.1 Intensity ratios (linear scale)

This can be achieved by merely taking the logarithm of the numbers involved. 10^9 becomes 9, 10^8 becomes 8, etc., on the log scale to the base 10 (and not to the base e, written on calculators as ln). Figure 3.2 shows the effect on our ratio bars; all are now accommodated in the same space. The decibel scale is a simple way of achieving this.

17

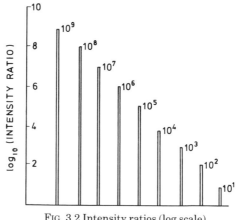

FIG. 3.2 Intensity ratios (log scale)

The vertical scale of Figure 2.7 is in the log form; with a linear scale many of the harmonics would not be seen.

The Decibel (dB)

The original way of measuring sound intensities, in terms of the bel, followed a procedure similiar to the one above. The ratio of the measured intensity (in W m^{-2}) to a reference intensity I_0 (taken as 10^{-12} W m^{-2}) was calculated. The bel was then defined as

$$\text{sound intensity level, in bels} = \log_{10} \frac{I}{I_0}$$

The bel was found to be an inconveniently large unit and so the decibel (0.1 bel) came into use:

$$\text{sound intensity level, in decibels} = 10 \log_{10} \frac{I}{I_0}$$

Once we have taken the logarithm, we talk of sound levels.

Calculation:

The romantic whisper of the last chapter gave an intensity at the ear of 8.0×10^{-7} W m^{-2}. The dB level would be:

$$10 \log \frac{8 \times 10^{-7}}{10^{-12}} = 10 \times 5.903 = 59 \text{ dB}.$$

Whatever else the whisper may lead to, it will not cause hearing damage. The shout produced an intensity of 8×10^{-5} W m^{-2}, and in dB:

$$10 \log \frac{8 \times 10^{-5}}{10^{-12}} = 10 \times 7.9 = 79 \text{ dB}.$$

Table 3.1 show how the wide range of intensity ratios for various environments (relative to the reference of 10^{-12} W m^{-2}) are reduced to a series of small numbers on the decibel scale.

TABLE 3.1 DECIBELS AND INTENSITY RATIOS

Intensity ratio	dB	Examples of noise source
1	0	Approximate threshold of hearing
10	10	
100	20	Very quiet rural, no wind
1,000	30	
10,000	40	Quiet office
100,000	50	Normal conversation at 1 m
1,000,000	60	Office
10,000,000	70	
100,000,000	80	Traffic
1,000,000,000	90	Lathes, typical process plant
10,000,000,000	100	Foundry, pneumatic drills
100,000,000,000	110	Woodworking shop
1,000,000,000,000	120	Boiler shop, engine room; discomfort
10,000,000,000,000	130	10 m to one side of a jet engine exhaust
100,000,000,000,000	140	Severe pain

This emphasises the point that a small decrease on the decibel scale corresponds to a large decrease in intensity (ie energy). This is an important fact to bear in mind when discussing reductions in noise level.

Most microphones measure acoustic pressure. We can easily adapt the equation for sound intensity level since the intensity depends on the square of the pressure. Replacing the two intensities we get:

$$\text{sound pressure level, in decibels} = 10 \log \frac{p^2}{p_0^2}$$

and since the log of a square of a number is just twice the log of the number,

$$\text{sound pressure level, in decibels} = 20 \log_{10} \frac{p}{p_0}$$

The reference pressure p_0 is taken as 2×10^{-5} Pa (or 20 μPa) and corresponds closely enough for practical purposes to the reference intensity of 10^{-12} W m^{-2}. This pressure is also conveniently close to that just detectable by the average healthy ear in its most sensitive frequency range.

With these consistent reference values, these equations for sound intensity level and sound pressure level give the same answers.

Calculation:

The rms pressure inside a tank is 40 Pa. What is the sound pressure level, in dB relative to 2×10^{-5} Pa?

$$\text{From the equation above, } 20 \log_{10} \frac{40}{2 \times 10^{-5}} = 20 \times 6.3 = 126 \text{ dB.}$$

Addition of Decibels

When more than one source is present we have to add levels in dB. The same calculation arises with a single source when we wish to add the levels in the various frequency bands making up the total sound; we will also use it in calculating the effective reduction given by a hearing protector. The basic problem is that decibels, being logarithmic units, cannot be added directly; two 70 dB sources (both fairly quiet) do not make 140 dB (extremely noisy).

It is the total intensity reaching us from all the contributions that is needed so we have to find the intensity of each one. To do this we merely turn round the equation for decibels:

$$\text{as intensity level (dB)} = 10 \log \frac{I_1}{I_0}, \text{ then } \frac{I_1}{I_0} = \text{antilog} \frac{(\text{level in dB})}{10}.$$

Calculation:

Two machines each generate an intensity level of 80 dB when running separately. What is the level when both are running?

$$\text{We have for one machine, } 80 = 10 \log \frac{I_1}{I_0} = 10 \log \frac{I_1}{10^{-12}}$$

$$\text{giving antilog} \left[\frac{80}{10} \right] = \frac{I_1}{10^{-12}}, \text{ and, since antilog } 8 = 10^8, I_1 = 10^{-4} \text{ W m}^{-2}.$$

With both machines running, we have double this intensity, i.e. 2×10^{-4} W m^{-2}. The dB value of this total is:

$$10 \log \frac{2 \times 10^4}{10^{-12}} = 10 \log (2 \times 10^8) = 83 \text{ dB.}$$

This is a far cry from adding the two 80 dBs to get 160 dB and it is closer to our experience of two moderately noisy sources sounding a little louder than either alone. This figure of 3 dB increase for doubling the energy involved is worth remembering because it also works the other way and a 3 dB reduction means a halving of the intensity concerned. Chapter 6 will use this to juggle intensity and time to reduce a noise dose.

Life is far too short to go through this performance for several sources or for the ten standard octave bands. The nomogram in Figure 3.3 is a good way of shortening the calculation and in fact of getting rid of some unnecessary data. To use this, we enter the nomogram from below at the number obtained by subtracting the lower of the two levels from the higher. We then read off the corresponding number above the line which is the amount to be added to the higher of the pair. Applying this to the two 80 dB machines the difference between them is zero and we add 3 dB to the higher and get 83 dB.

Amount to be added to higher level to obtain total (dB).

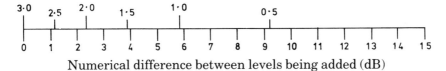

Numerical difference between levels being added (dB)

FIG. 3.3 Nomogram for adding decibels

If we are realistic about the sort of measurements we might make in military vehicles or around weapons, workshops or airfields, we are unlikely to get an accuracy of better than 0.5 dB. The measured values will vary from place and between repeated measurements at the same place. A significant feature of the nomogram is that it tells us that if two levels differ by more than 10 dB, the lower one contributes less than 0.5 dB to the *total* level and can usually be ignored.

Example: Four independent noise sources in a tracked vehicle give respective sound levels of 94, 88, 96 and 84 dB. Estimate the total resulting sound level.

Using the nomogram, we can ignore the contribution of the 84 dB since it is more than 10 dB below the highest measured component (96 dB). In tabular form we can combine the remaining pairs as follows:

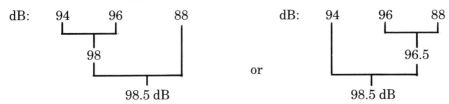

and it is immaterial in which order we chose to do the pairing.

The reader could also try the following precedure for adding two levels:
▶ Take the first level in dB.
▶ Divide by 10.
▶ Take the antilog, call it A.
▶ Take the second level in dB.
▶ Divide by 10.
▶ Take the antilog, call it B.
▶ Add A and B, call it C.
▶ Find the logarithm of C and multiply by 10.

As an exercise, you might like to:
● extend this calculation for any number of levels; and
● write a programme for a microcomputer to do this for you.

Later in this book we will meet occasions where we do appear to be simply adding values in dB. We do this, for instance, in calculating effectiveness of hearing protectors, or in calculating sound transmission through a partition. Although it looks like an addition, it is in fact a multiplication (remember that $(\log x) + (\log y) = \log (xy)$). We will use this first in considering two frequency-dependent weightings, the 'A' and 'C' weightings, where we effectively multiply the sound we measure by the weighting factors.

The 'A' and 'C' Weightings

The dB level measured by a good microphone should be independent of the frequencies present in the sound, which means that the microphone sensitivity or response does not change with frequency over the usual measuring range. This is shown as a horizontal line in Figure 3.4. The ear has a response, however, that falls off drastically at low frequencies. Electronic weighting, using simple filters, can be applied to a microphone output so that it behaves very approximately as an ear. This A-weighted curve has become the standard measure of the loudness of the sound and, although it was not originally derived for this purpose, of likely effects on the ear. All measurements on this scale are written as dB(A).

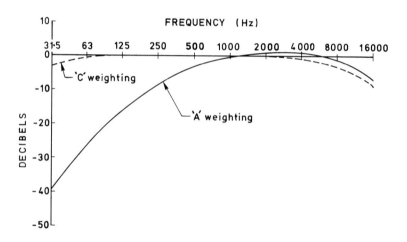

FIG. 3.4 'A' and 'C' weighting curves

The 'C' weighting, sometimes provided on sound level meters and also shown in Figure 3.4, influences only the highest and lowest frequencies and provides an almost flat, but precisely specified, response. The difference between db(A) and dB(C) levels is a rough guide to the low frequency content. The 'B' weighting, which is historic, and the 'D' weighting, which is used only for aircraft noise, are omitted from the figure.

The conversion of a measured dB value to dB(A) can only be done if we know how the energy is divided between the various frequencies, because the correction factor applied depends on frequency. The corrections are conventionally made for the standard octave bands encountered earlier and have the following values:

TABLE 3.2 CONVERSION OF dB TO dB (A)

Centre frequency (Hz)	31.5	63	125	250	500	1000	2000	4000	8000	16000
Correction dB to dB (A)	−39	−26	−16	−9	−3	0	+1	+1	−1	−7

The effect of the dB to dB (A) conversion clearly depends on the dominant frequencies present in the noise. A dominant high frequency whine at about 1000 Hz will give similar dB and dB (A) levels but lower frequency exhaust noise, track noise and helicopter rotor noise will produce very different dB and dB (A) values. For example, sound level measurements inside a hovering Chinook gave these results, neglecting the 16 kHz band in which the levels were very low.

Centre frequency (Hz)	31.5	63	125	250	500	1000	2000	4000	8000	Total
dB	109	97	99	104	99	106	105	96	90	114
We now apply the dB (A) corrections:										
dB to dB (A)	−39	−26	−16	−9	−3	0	+1	+1	−1	
to get the component sounds in dB (A):										
dB (A)	70	71	83	95	96	106	106	97	89	109

Running the eye along the original data in dB, we see that the microphone senses significant low frequency energy. The ear hears quite a different spectrum, with energy mainly at the higher frequency end.

This Chinook data does not tell the whole story as nothing has been said about how the data were obtained. Experience in such an environment indicates marked variations in sound level from place to place, and from time to time as the engine power and blade angle vary. The noise hazard will depend on where an individual sits and for how long. There would also have been exposure to the ground-running power unit just above the rear door used for embarkation; this unit produces about 110 dB (A).

A further example comes from a recovery vehicle. The same total dB level was obtained behind the vehicle, 2m from the exhaust, and in the vehicle at the winch-operators position:

Frequency (Hz)	31.5	63	125	250	500	1000	2000	4000	8000	Total dB
2m behind	95	98	84	80	76	74	70	64	56	99
Inside vehicle	90	94	98	91	87	85	83	76	66	99

The heavier weighting against the predominant lower frequencies, especially the 63 Hz contribution in the first position, compared with the 125 Hz in the second, results in the respective measured dB (A) values of 80 dB (A) and 91 dB (A).

At this stage it is useful to get a 'feel' for the dB (A), not only to appreciate this text but also when using the ear as the most readily available tool to estimate the possibility of a noise hazard. If it is necessary to shout to be heard at a range of 3m, the sound level is 75 to 80 dB (A); at a range of 1 m it will be 85 to 90 dB (A). The latter condition is a rough indication that the specified noise limits for hearing hazard are being reached. The ear should never be used as a sound measuring device at levels above this!

Summary

We have examined the use of the decibel scales which are vital for discussing noise problems. The reader should now be aware of the distinction between dB and dB (A), have a feel for dB (A) values and be able to solve most of the following problems.

SELF TEST QUESTIONS

Question 1   The rms pressure inside a tracked vehicle is 16 Pa.
(a) What is the dB level re 2×10^{-5} Pa?
(b) Does this figure tell you how loud it seems?

Answer ....

....

....

Question 2   In a workshop, one noise source produces a sound pressure level of
90 dB at a point and a second source 95 dB. What is the resulting
calculated sound pressure level? Check your calculation against
the nomogram of Fig. 3.3.

Answer ....

....

....

Question 3   A meter gives an unweighted sound pressure level of 100 dB and an
A-weighted one of 70 dB (A). Comment on the frequency content of
the noise.

Answer ....

....

....

Question 4   An airfield ground power unit gave the following octave band data
at a range of 1 m

Centre frequency:	31.5	63	125	250	500	1000	2000	4000	8000	Hz
Sound level:	80	93.5	100	94	100	95	88	82	78	dB

Estimate the overall level in dB.
Answer ....

....

....

Question 5   Octave band frequency analysis in a armoured personnel carrier
                 gave the following data:

Centre frequency:	31.5	63	125	250	500	1000	2000	4000	8000	Hz
Sound level:	90	102	102	101	96	91	85	83	70	dB

Correct these values to dB(A). What is the total level in dB(A)?

Answer ....

....

....

Question 6   The following data were obtained at two positions close to a Jet
                 Provost aircraft during ground training, one directly in front and
                 one about 135° round towards the rear. Wind noise made it impos-
                 sible to take meaningful measurements in the 31.5 Hz octave band.

Centre frequency:	31.5	63	125	250	500	1000	2000	4000	8000	Hz
Sound level:										
In front:	—	76	85	90	91	95	104.5	104.5	106	dB
At 135°:	—	91	95	99	99	95	97.5	92.5	89	dB

Estimate the levels in dB(A) at the two positions. What differences
would you notice between these sounds?

Answer ....

....

....

Answers on page 112.

4. The Ear and Hearing

This chapter discusses the way in which the ear functions and describes critically the audiometric techniques for measuring the sensitivity of hearing. The effect of noise on this sensitivity is then surveyed, to indicate the qualities of the noise that are responsible.

The Outer Ear

The overall structure of the ear is shown in Figure 4.1. Working from the outside in, the floppy exterior pinna can act as a directional sound-gathering device at high frequencies. It would be much improved by the addition of an ear-lid, analogous to eyelids, which could be used to keep sound out. It can be significant for people sleeping in a noisy environment (e.g. aboard ship) that the ear does not switch off and recuperate.

Incident pressure waves are transmitted along the auditory canal to the eardrum (tympanic membrane). The ear canal is about 3 cm long, closed at the far end by the eardrum and open to atmospheric pressure at the outer end. It is important that atmospheric pressure normally prevails on the both sides of the eardrum, hence the eustachian tube connecting with the throat. This tube is normally closed by the soft palate but swallowing will open the palate to allow pressures to equalise when the external air pressure changes suddenly. The innermost section of the canal has a bony wall which is very sensitive to the insertion of an ear plug. The discomfort produced gives early warning that a plug is being inserted too deep. Wax is secreted by cells in the canal lining to trap dust etc.; an accumulation of this wax can cause an apparent hearing loss. The canal acts as resonator and amplifier for a broad band of frequencies centred around 3000 Hz.

The Middle Ear

The motion of the eardrum is transmitted to a second membrane (the oval window) via three small bones (ossicles). These ossicles help to transmit acoustic pres-

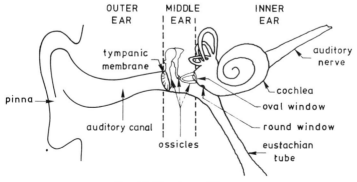

FIG. 4.1 Structure of the ear

sure between the air in the outer ear and the liquid in the inner ear beyond the oval window. Two muscles (part of the aural reflex) can prevent excessive motion of these bones due to an intense sound. It takes time for the muscle system to respond, however, and this time (~25 ms) will be longer than the rise-time of acoustic pressure from a weapon, hence the great hazard of weapon noise (Chapter 7). The aural reflex does not stay on, however, for sustained continuous sound.

The Inner Ear

The oval window is one end of a spiral liquid-filled tube about 3 cm long (called the cochlea since it resembles a tiny snail) which is divided into two parts by the basilar membrane running most of the way along it. Waves travel inward through the liquid above the membrane, and outward beneath it to the round window. En route, waves are set up in the membrane, stressing the hair cells it carries. These cells generate signals which are transmitted by the auditory nerve to the brain. Different regions of the cells are excited by different frequencies, those nearest the oval window particularly by the higher frequencies. The brain's perception of loudness depends on how much the hairs are stressed and the perception of frequency by their position on the membrane. Intense sound can cause excessive motion of the hair cells and eventually permanent damage. The initial issue of about 32,000 cells cannot be replaced or repaired.

If a region is already stressed due to one sound it is less able to react to a second sound. This *masking* is important in sentry duty and in communication (dealt with in Chapter 11).

It is not necessary for sound to travel along the external ear/eardrum/ossicles route in order to excite the receptors of the inner ear. Sound can enter the body through the skin and superficial tissue but the fraction of the incident energy achieving this is small due to the acoustic properties of the body surface. The most significant contribution is via bone conduction within the skull and this sets a theoretical limit to the effectiveness of hearing protectors such as ear plugs and muffs. Bone conduction is the main mechanism by which we hear our own voices, hence the unfamiliar sound of our tape recorded voices due to play-back via air.

Frequency Characteristics

The ear is more sensitive to some frequencies than to others. To measure these frequency characteristics we have to find the level in dB of a pure tone that is just audible and repeat this at a number of frequencies. This gives the *threshold of hearing* curve (dashed line in Figure 4.2). It is this threshold curve that is raised when noise causes hearing loss and we need a higher acoustic pressure before we can detect the sound. We note that the ear is most sensitive at around 3 kHz. Another significant feature is its relative insensitivity below 200 Hz; this is useful as it is difficult to remove low frequency sound energy by conventional simple means.

We can also find the level of sounds of various frequencies that are judged equally loud, and hence construct 'equal-loudness contours'. A selection of such contours are included in Figure 4.2. Again higher pressures are needed at low frequencies to get a sound as loud as one at, say, 1kHz. The A-weighting curve of

Chapter 3 resembles the equal-loudness contours for faint sounds turned upside down.

Normal ears can just detect the change in loudness due to a 1 dB change in sound pressure level. A change of 10 dB gives approximately a halving or doubling of loudness.

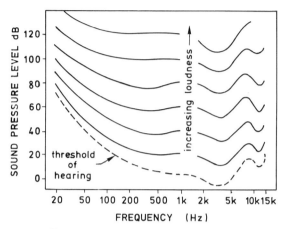

FIG. 4.2   Frequency response of the ear

Measurement of Hearing — Audiometry

There is no single test which will tells us all about the effectiveness of someone's hearing. Where it is necessary to diagnose the nature of hearing loss, audiology clinics will use a number of different tests. However, one test stands out as being especially useful; this is the determination of the threshold of hearing (that is, the faintest sound which can just be heard) for pure-tone sounds at various frequencies, yielding the pure-tone audiogram. This is by far the most commonly used test of hearing, and the only one suitable for routine use as part of a hearing conversation programme.

The procedure for finding the pure-tone audiogram is largely standardised. The tones are generated by a instrument called an 'audiometer' and presented, through headphones, to each ear separately. The frequencies used are 0.5, 1, 2, 3, 4, and 6 kHz, sometimes with 250 Hz and/or 8 kHz as well. Usually the low frequencies are presented first, although the order is sometimes changed; it is useful to give a practice session with a 1 kHz tone first. Usually the left ear is tested first, then the right. Figure 4.3 shows a typical audiometric system.

The threshold ('hearing level') is found by starting with a tone at a level the subject can hear, then gradually decreasing its level until the subject signals that he can no longer hear it; the level is then gradually increased until the subject can hear it, then decreased again, and so on until the threshold has been crossed from above and below several times. The subject sometimes requires a little practice. The level of the tone may be controlled by an operator but in self-recording audiometers the machine itself can decrease or increase the level depending on whether the subject presses a button to indicate he can hear the tone, as shown by the dashed line in Figure 4.3. This generates the zig-zag trace of Figure 4.4; the threshold is halfway up the trace. About 30 s is spent at each frequency. Recently, audiometers with a microprocessor control have become available which give a print-out of hearing level.

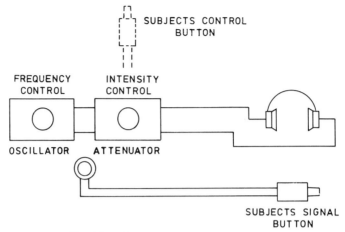

FIG 4.3. Audiometric system (schematic)

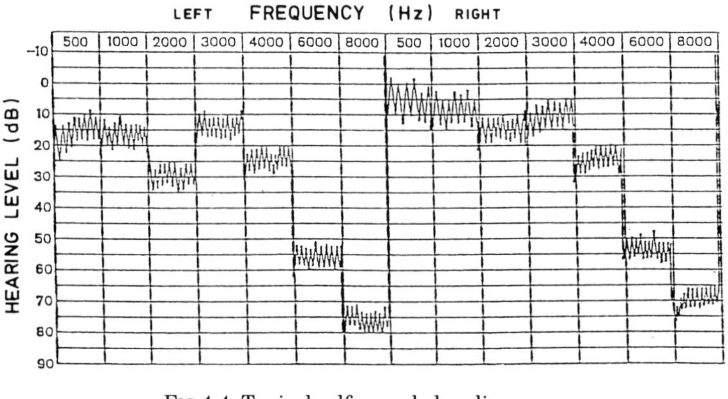

FIG 4.4. Typical self-recorded audiogram

The hearing level is expressed in decibels, with 0 dB as nominally 'normal'. 0 dB in this case does NOT refer to the usual reference pressure of 20 μPa, but to the average hearing level of young adults with no sign or history of ear disease or noise exposure. Hearing levels vary between different individuals and if they lie within 10 or 15 dB of the nominal 0 dB can be considered as acceptable. For calibration purposes, the 0 dB levels are translated into the corresponding sound pressure levels produced by headphones placed on 'artificial ear' couplers.

Audiometric measurements can be inaccurate. One problem is the location of the audiometer in a room without a suitably low noise background. An empty room that sounds quiet may well be inadequate. Typical octave band sound pressure levels not to be exceeded in an audiometric test room are shown in Table 4.1.

TABLE 4.1 MAXIMUM SOUND LEVELS IN AUDIOMETRIC ROOMS

Octave band centre frequency, Hz		31.5	63	125	250	500	1000	2000	4000	8000
Octave band sound pressure level, dB	} {	76	62	48	36	14	16	29	37	32
		76	62	55	44	31	31	43	50	44

Two sets of figures for the maximum sound pressure levels are given. The upper set refers to normal audiometric headphones. The lower set refers to headphones fitted with 'Audiocups', which are ear-muff-like surrounds for the headphones to reduce background noise at the ears. It is essential, in using surrounds of this type, that the earphones make proper contact on the ear, otherwise the audiograms will be inaccurate.

Octave band sound pressure levels greater than Table 4.1 will mask the test tone, making it impossible to measure the more sensitive hearing levels. Since most rooms in military units will exceed the levels shown in Table 4.1, a sound-proofed audiometric booth is usually needed.

There may also be problems due to a lack of concentration by the subject, or a lack of familiarity with the technique, that may well require discarding the first audiogram and averaging several more. Accuracy may be improved by removing and replacing the headphones between each test, giving the subject a short rest period between each. Variations of ± 5 dB, or even ± 10 dB, between audiograms are common. Careful explanation of the test is needed in the preliminary briefing. There may also be a desire by the subject to provide answers that lessen a known threshold shift that could mean medical regrading; this is a recognised reason for absenteeism from audiogram tests. On the other hand, the apparent sudden growth of threshold shift may accompany the likelihood of financial compensation. Various measurement procedures can reveal such stratagems.

If qualified medical personnel are available, they should inspect the ear canal and ear drum, and remove any excessive build-up of wax. This must NEVER be attempted by unqualified personnel.

A checklist to ensure that the audiograms produced have some meaning is as follows:

AUDIOMETRY CHECKLIST
▶ Has the audiometer been calibrated during the previous 12 months, and are the earphones used with it the correct ones?
▶ Has the operator checked it against his own known hearing levels, or against a colleague's hearing levels, on the day of the test?
▶ Is the noise level at the subject's position low enough (see Table 4.1)?
▶ Has the operator checked that the subject:
   (a) is not suffering from a cold, sore throat or sinusitus;
   (b) has not been exposed to intense noise (including discotheques!) over the previous 24 h?

▶ If the initial audiogram shows a substantial change since the previous test (or, if the subject has not done a test previously, the initial audiogram indicates poor hearing) has the audiogram been repeated after a short rest period?

If the answer to any of the above is 'no', you are not taking an audiogram, you are generating waste paper!

Example

Figure 4.4 was for a soldier aged 40 with 24 yr service, working with rifles on an outdoor range, machine guns in an indoor range, 105 mm gun, 30 mm cannon, armoured personnel carriers and some vehicle maintenance. There is a definite high-frequency hearing loss in both ears, although since the loss is mainly above 3 kHz, the ability to understand speech is only slightly affected. The steady decrease in threshold during the 500 Hz left ear sequence is due to a learning process. The final 1000 Hz tone, not expected by the subject, serves as a check on the earlier result. The 2000 Hz left ear loss is unusual in being greater than the loss at 3 kHz and would be checked by a repeat measurement.

While the interpretation of audiograms is a specialised medical task, any audiometric programme must be organised so that data is properly filed for future comparison. Personnel working in known hazardous areas are obvious candidates for particularly careful observation but the appropriate procedures must be set up to ensure that their audiometric progress is monitored and that all hazardous areas are identified. Audiograms can also provide a useful way of indicating to an individual that he needs to take particular care to wear protection. Feedback from audiometry should form an integral part of any hearing conservation programme.

Causes of Hearing Loss

The common causes of hearing loss are:

    ▶ Congenital — this should not be of much interest for military purposes as individuals with congenital deafness should not be accepted for military service nor placed in noisy employments.

    ▶ Conductive — generally due to infection or bony growth (otosclerosis) in the middle ear. It usually affects hearing at all frequencies and requires medical attention. It may also be caused temporarily by colds, throat infections, catarrh or hay fever.

    ▶ Noise exposure — loss is usually greatest at 4 kHz or 6 kHz, sometimes at 3 kHz or 8 kHz.

    ▶ Inner ear disease — typically causes greatest losses at high frequencies.

    ▶ Ageing — again, typically causes greatest losses at high frequencies. It should not be a problem in personnel of military age.

    ▶ Head injury.

    ▶ Certain drugs, especially those used to treat very serious infections.

    ▶ Wax or other obstructions in the ear canal. The cure is obvious but must only be undertaken by medical personnel.

A number of other causes are possible, and diagnosis on the basis of a pure-tone audiogram should not be attemped. Diagnosis and, where possible, treatment should only be conducted by qualified medical personnel. As a general rule, hearing loss should always be referred for medical opinion; however, the audiogram should first be repeated after a few days interval to ensure that the loss did not result from a temporary condition, such as a cold, or from the subject's lack of familiarity with audiometry.

Noise Induced Hearing Loss (Continuous Noise)

Exposure to excessive noise has a number of effects on hearing. It impairs the ability to distinguish different frequencies, distorts the perception of loudness, and can cause an apparent 'ringing' (tinnitus) in the ears. The most easily measured effect, however, is that the hearing threshold is raised so that faint sounds can no longer be heard. This threshold shift (TS) depends on the intensity, duration and frequency content of the noise. It is usually greatest around 3, 4 or 6kHz but, when due to noise from weapons, may be greatest at 8 kHz; which frequency is most affected depends to some extent on the frequency content of the noise. Some individuals are, for reasons not yet fully understood, much more susceptible to noise-induced hearing loss than others.

In a quiet period following noise exposure, some degree of recovery takes place; if the noise exposure was not too severe, this recovery can apparently be complete, and we can speak of a temporary threshold shift (TTS). However, if the exposure is frequently repeated (especially where exposure takes place before recovery from the previous exposure is complete) the threshold shift will eventually become permanent (PTS). A single, very intense, exposure will give a large TS which may fail to recover completely, leaving a residual PTS.

Recovery times for TTS depend to some extent on the noise which caused it; there are also differences in recovery patterns between different individuals and between the same individuals on different occasions. In general, smaller values of TTS recover more quickly.

If the TTS is very large, recovery might take some days or weeks, and some remaining PTS is likely. Any TS persisting after a month or two is likely to be permanent, although there have been reports of partial recovery over longer periods.

Low frequencies are less damaging than higher frequencies; with the latter, levels around 80 dB may cause some degree of TS if the exposure lasts several hours.

Threshold shift from noise exposure is caused primarily by injury to the hair cells on the basilar membrane within the cochlea, and is therefore classified as a 'nerve' hearing loss. PTS is associated with wholesale destruction of, or serious damage to, the hair cells over part of the basilar membrane. These cells do not regenerate and cannot be repaired. The nature of the damage leads to sound being perceived as distorted, in such a way that amplifying the sound (as by a hearing aid) gives little or no benefit.

In industrial practice, it is generally assumed that PTS is the important quantity and TTS is largely disregarded. TTS can however be important in military practice; for instance, troops leaving a noisy personnel carrier or helicopter may well have a TTS which, in addition to any PTS they may have, will impair military effectiveness.

The noise-induced permanent threshold shift (excluding age effects) shown in the upper curve of Figure 4.5 would be exceeded by 10% of the working population exposed to continuous noise of 90 dB (A) over a 30-yr, 8-h-day working period. Typically the shift starts at around 4 kHz and deepens (worsens) and spreads towards conversational frequencies as the years of exposure go by. Note that the 90 dB (A) 8-h criterion is not protecting a large number of people from a substantial hearing loss.

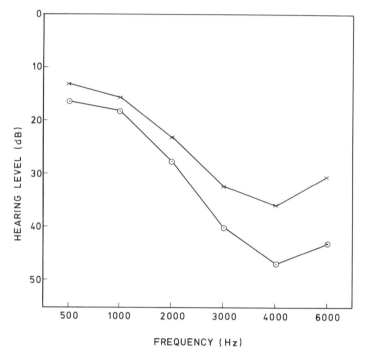

FIG. 4.5 Permanent hearing loss

Age Effects

As exposure to noise continues, the hearing mechanism also deteriorates naturally due to ageing, in particular the sensing hair cells close to the oval window have worn out. This means a gradual deafness at high frequencies is creeping in. As with other aspects of hearing, however, there is a very large variation between individuals.

The lower curve of Figure 4.5 shows the effect of adding the expected ageing effect for a 50-yr-old population to the noise-induced threshold shift. The effects of disease would make the hearing levels in a typical population substantially worse than this.

These two curves show that a noise-induced loss acquired *but not noticed* when young may give a hearing disability later when the inevitable age-related loss is added on. The fact that early hearing losses are not noticed is a great problem in ensuring that prescribed hearing protection is actually worn. If pain resulted from such injury, the case would be very different, but aural pain does not occur until sound levels are above the level for possible damage.

Predicting PTS

It has long been hoped that the temporary threshold shift could be correlated directly with permanent threshold shift, so that long-term predictions of PTS could be made from TTS measurements. An enormous amount of experimental work has been carried out on TTS, but the only useful conclusions seem to be that exposures which do not produce TTS are unlikely, after repeated occasions of exposure, to produce much PTS; and that, for noise exposures typical of industrial practice (continuous noise over most of the working day), the TTS measured 2 min after one exposure is approximately equal to eventual PTS after many years. These conclusions hold only for average values of TTS and PTS measured for large numbers of men, and are *NOT* necessarily valid for individuals.

The relation between continuous noise and hearing damage has been evaluated chiefly by studying the PTS data of workers in noisy factories. There are several problems in this approach; the noise varies between different jobs (in level, frequency content, duration and in the presence of impulsive components); their total noise exposure may have included exposure outside working hours on noisy hobbies such as shooting; their initial hearing levels are not known and have to be assumed to be 'normal'; their measured hearing levels will include loss due to disease and/or ageing. Together with the variation in susceptibility between different individuals, this makes interpretation of the results difficult.

Another limitation is that some surveys attempt to exclude any individual with evidence for, or a history of, any ear disease; the interaction of noise exposure and disease is therefore largely unknown.

TS from Weapon Noise

PTS from weapon noise exposure is even more difficult to assess since the details of the exposure are usually known only approximately. Here we are forced to use TTS as an indicator of hazard. Any experiments to measure TTS for a known exposure have obviously to be conducted with the utmost care to avoid undue risk of producing PTS; it is thus recommended that the TTS measured within a few minutes of exposure should never exceed 25 dB, and that complete recovery should never take more than 24 h; no noise exposure should be permitted during the recovery period. At one time the use of much larger values of TTS was accepted, but it is now recognised that this carries some risk of permanent damage.

Figure 4.6 shows a series of threshold measurements in one unprotected ear of one subject exposure to the noise of seven rounds from an 81 mm mortar. Only results for frequencies of 2 kHz and above are shown since lower frequencies were little affected. These data were obtained some years ago; such a severe noise exposure and the resulting large values of TTS would not now be permitted.

The TTS is greatest measured soon (in this case, nominally 2 min) after exposure, and recovers as time goes on. However, some TS persists at 6 kHz after 22 h, indicating a risk of PTS at this frequency. (The data also show an improvement at 4 kHz measured 22 h after exposure, compared with the pre-exposure audiogram; has listening to the noise improved hearing, or is it more likely that the apparent improvement is due to errors in audiometry?)

The data refer to one subject only; some subjects might have shown less TTS, others more, and in some cases a large PTS could well have resulted.

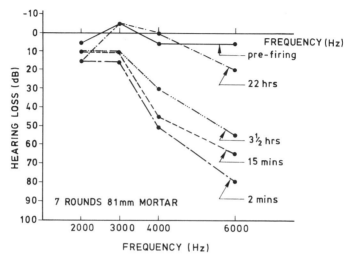

FIG. 4.6 Threshold shift due to mortar fire
(after Brasher P.F., *Journal RAMC*, Vol. 115, p. 167, 1965)

Actual Weapon Noise Effects

In the present context it is worth mentioning the data obtained from the 1982 Falkland Islands operation. Here identifiable military operations were carried out by men with previously known hearing thresholds. The operation also involved a considerable density of fire. For instance, over 1000 mortar bombs were fired by some mortars during the advance on Port Stanley and a similar number of shells from some artillery weapons. Thousands of rounds of 0.5″ machine gun fire were used at Tumbledown and there was in some places considerable use of anti-armour weapons. A questionnaire, clinical examination and audiometric testing were used 8 months after the conflict to establish the resulting noise induced hearing losses. These resulted in nine of the 205 men fully investigated being unfit for front-line military service on the Services hearing criterion; many others showed hearing loss of lesser magnitude. Details are given in J. R. Brown's article in the *Journal of Occupational Medicine*, Vol. 35, pp. 44–54, 1985.

Summary

Noise has been shown to cause shifts in the threshold of hearing that may be temporary or permanent. These add to the loss of hearing with age. The problem now is to identify a way of relating the characteristics of the noise to the likely hearing loss, and hence to be able to limit the noise exposure to non-hazardous levels.

5. Basic Noise Measurements

This chapter summarises the precautions needed to obtain meaningful sound level measurement using the simple types of sound level meter that may be available at unit level. Experience and specialised training are needed, as well as more complicated equipment, to carry out full-scale surveys. Weapon noise measurement requires it own specialised equipment and is discussed in more detail in Chapter 7.

Sound Level Meters

Although the human ear is very good at analysing sounds, it is a very bad measuring instrument in the sense that it cannot reliably measure the intensity of a sound. Hence, we need instruments that can produce a reliable quantitive measure of noise. The most basic and most widely used instrument is the sound level meter. One is shown being used to measure the octave band spectrum close to a tank in Figure 5.1.

FIG. 5.1 Use of a sound level meter

The basic components of a sound level meter are shown in Figure 5.2 and will be discussed in turn.

FIG. 5.2 Components of a sound level meter

Microphones

Most microphones used for noise measurement are of the capacitance (condenser) type, in which a very thin metal diaphragm is mounted close to a rigid backplate to form an electrical capacitance. The capacitance varies inversely with the distance between the diaphragm and the backplate, so that when the diaphragm moves in response to acoustic pressure, the capacitance also changes. A constant electrical charge is placed on the backplate, so that changes in capacitance result in a change in voltage. These voltages can be amplified, with the amplifier placed very close to the backplate, since the microphone capacitance is small and losses in the cable between the backplate and the amplifier would otherwise be substantial. The advantages of capacitance microphones are the stability of their sensitivity and their wide frequency response.

The microphone should give a flat frequency response over as wide a range as possible. In general the larger the microphone diaphragm the more sensitive it is. Small microphones (¼" or less) need to be used for very high frequencies, above about 20 kHz, as with small-arms measurements. Small microphones are also less directional in their response.

Electronics and Display

The amplifier/attenuator network following the microphone provides voltages in a range that can be easily handled by the weighting, averaging and display components.

The weighting network gives a choice of 'A' or 'C' [written as dB (A) and dB (C)]. If the frequency response of the microphone and other components justifies it, 'Linear' weighting (written as dB) may be provided. It is essential that data are clearly recorded as dB or dB (A) etc.

The display (a needle or digital read-out) cannot follow very rapid voltage fluctuations, and even if it could, the eye could not follow them. The acoustic pressure fluctuations can therefore be displayed as the root-mean-square (rms) average met in Chapter 2, either with a 'slow' setting of 1s averaging time or a 'fast' setting of 125 ms averaging time.

Some meters also provide an 'impulse' setting with a 35 ms averaging time combined with a slow decay to allow the display to be read. The original intention of this setting was in the assessment of loudness of industrial impulse noise; it is now of little use in routine noise measurement.

Some sound level meters also have a 'peak' setting which displays the maximum instantaneous pressure in dB. The main use of this is in identifying peak pressures above a criterion level where corresponding action is required; for instance, the 1986 European Community directive requires use of hearing protection if the peak pressure exceeds 140 dB (0.2 kPa).

Some sound level meters also include an overload indicator, to show when the meter display can no longer be relied on. This is most likely to happen when the noise has impulsive components.

Sound level meters are sometimes equipped with the octave or one-third octave band filters discussed earlier. In practice, the use of such filters can be quite difficult and time-consuming, especially if the noise level is fluctuating.

Accuracy of Sound Level Meters

International Standard 651 (BS 5969) specifies various grades of sound level meter, as follows:

Type 0: Laboratory standard.

Type 1: Precision.

Type 2: General applications (industrial).

Type 3: Suitable for preliminary noise surveys only, to determine whether a noise limit has been violated.

There is little to be gained from undue precision. Differences due to measurement position, which can rarely be specified exactly, and fluctuating levels are generally large enough to make a Type 2 meter adequate in the present context.

The accuracy of a sound level meter's readings depends on a number of factors. The main source of error, especially for sources with a marked high-frequency content, is likely to be the variation in microphone response with its orientation to the source. This variation tends to be less with small microphones and the use of a 'half-inch' (12.7 mm o.d.) rather than a 'one-inch' (25 mm o.d.) microphone is recommended.

Whatever grade of meter is employed, it should be thoroughly checked and calibrated (including the accuracy of range switches and weighting networks) at regular intervals, for instance every year. The calibrator used to check the meter function at the beginning and end of each measurement also needs to be calibrated against a known standard; while it is unusual for these calibrators to change their output, it can happen!

Windshields

Turbulence due to wind causes a spurious low-frequency signal which, besides giving a misleading result, can easily overload the meter. A porous windshield placed over the microphone, as in Figure 5.1, will reduce this, but even with a windshield, it is not possible to measure low-level sounds in windy conditions.

Fluctuating Sound Levels

Fluctuations in sound level with time are usually present and are a nuisance. In the short time scale they can make it difficult to estimate a needle reading. On a longer time scale they raise the whole problem of how representative of the sound is the segment of time that was actually covered. The same proviso holds for tape recordings of such noise.

Variations in power level of machinery provide obvious examples in workshops and vehicles. The tank travelling at various speeds in various gears over variable terrain is a familiar example; even when travelling only over a tarmac surface, variations of ±5 dB (A) were found for a single measurement position. A fire tender travelling from hanger to runway exposed the crew in the forward section to sound levels varying from 76 dB (A) to 96 dB (A), the latter on a straight run at speed. In these circumstances an on-site octave band measurement sequence is hopeless and the sound has to be recorded for later analysis in the laboratory.

Fluctuating levels are best dealt with by the integrating sound level meter which samples the sound at regular small intervals of time and works out the equivalent continuous sound level for the measurement duration. These instruments are usually expensive. If it has to be moved around with the worker from one noise environment to another during the working day, it is much better to use a noise dosemeter, a simpler, smaller and cheaper version of the integrating meter. The concept of the integrating sound level meter and of the dosemeter is more fully described in Chapter 6.

Tape Recordings

Tape recordings are especially useful when the noise level is fluctuating, or where the noise must be analysed in terms of octave, one-third octave or narrower bands. The main disadvantages are that the noise must be analysed subsequently in the laboratory, and the limitations of the tape recorder, particularly its frequency response, must be known and allowed for.

Any high-quality portable tape recorder can be used. Most sound level meters have a socket for a tape recorder input. During recording, the meter weighting should be set to linear (or 'C' if a linear weighting is not available). Reel-to-reel machines are commonly used, but a good quality cassette recorder can be used if necessary. Digital tape recorders can also be used. The recorder must be maintained in good condition; in particular, the tape heads must be kept clean. It is worthwhile using one channel of the recorder as a speech channel for recording details of measurement conditions, such as meter settings and the presence of other intruding sources, as recording progresses, as well as keeping a notebook. The frequency response of the tape recorder must be known; this depends to some extent on the type of tape. Response to low frequencies can be poor and may limit the use of the recorder when the noise has important low-frequency components. Tape hiss may give an indication of high-frequency noise not present in the original signal. Dolby settings should not be used. Beware that a slow tape speed used to economise on tape may unacceptably degrade the high frequency response.

Analysis of the tape recording can be conducted using a sound level meter equipped with octave or one-third octave band filters, and using the same part of the recording, possibly located from a recorded commentary, for each band. A real-time analyser can perform this task for all bands simultaneously. Use of a chart recorder gives a useful indication of the variation of level with time.

Very specialised (and expensive!) types of tape recorder are required for use with gunfire noise, as explained in Chapter 7.

Calibration

It is essential that the whole measuring system is calibrated immediately before and after a measurement. If the final check is not done on-site at the time there is no way of knowing whether a calibration change detected days later did in fact affect the results. There are two main types of calibrator:

▶ Electroacoustic:
typically a 1000 Hz source giving 94 dB [and hence 94 dB (A) as well, as there is no difference between the scales at this frequency]. This can also be used to calibrate dosemeters by applying its signal for a given time. Typical accuracy is ± 0.5 dB.

► Pistonphone:
often a 250 Hz, 124 dB source which calibrates at a level closer to many hazardous noises but which will need a 9 dB reduction to provide dB (A) values. These are rather more expensive and are justified when higher accuracy is needed, typically ± 0.2 dB.

Any tape recording should always begin and end with a calibration tone.

Noise Survey Checklist

All noise measurements should follow a precise procedure to ensure that the results are reliable:

► Check that any batteries are satisfactorily charged.
► Calibrate the measurement system.
► Sketch the measurement position, which is usually at the position of the operator's head with the operator absent, relative to the sources and reflecting surfaces.
► Check the background level and ensure that it is low enough to not affect the measurements. It should be 10 dB below source level at the measurement point. In outdoor measurements, note the effect of wind noise on the microphone and use a windshield in any case.
► Carry out measurements on the source noting any operational settings of the latter; relate any changes in these to measured variations in the sound level. Include dB or dB (A), slow or fast settings. Ensure that there are no effects due to your own, or any well-wisher's, body by using a tripod to support the meter (Figure 5.1) or holding it at arms length (and dimissing well-wishers). Keep an ear and eye open for other sources which might unexpectedly intrude.
► If using a tape recorder, ensure that settings of attenuators and the recording speed are noted, as well as the zero of the sound level meter scale supplying the signal.
► Calibrate the measurement system.

All measurement details should be carefully recorded in a log which can be used for future reference. Jottings on the back of envelopes will be lost and details not recorded at the time will be forgotten.

6. Hearing Conservation and Noise Limits

The Problem

We have so far established the decibel scale and discussed the measurement of noise and its general effect on hearing. It is now necessary to identify at what level, and for how long, the noise exposure can continue without being hazardous.

Occupational Noise Standards

The amount of threshold shift depends on the A-weighted sound pressure level and the duration of the noise producing it. Occupational noise standards are concerned with relating this to irrecoverable hearing loss due to nerve cell damage in the inner ear. The handicap imposed by hearing loss may be measured solely in terms of response to speech, and this is the basis of allowable civilian losses over a working lifetime. The Services take a wider view however and also consider the higher frequencies (4 and 6 kHz) involved in combat sounds.

Noise Dose

The hazardous effect of noise on hearing is now related to the 'noise dose' in which the average sound level (the size of spoon) and the duration of exposure (number of spoons per day) are combined and traded against one another. The first basic assumption is that the dB (A) is the appropriate measurement unit; the second, that a real-life fluctuating noise exposure pattern, involving various sound levels for various times, can be replaced by some average value. This average is taken as the notional sound level, unchanging over the period concerned, which would have the same acoustic energy as the actual fluctuating sound. It is termed

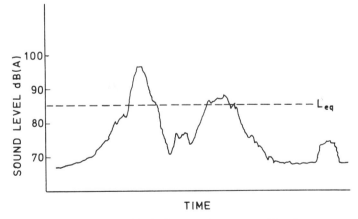

FIG. 6.1 Equivalent continuous sound level

43

the equivalent continuous sound level (ECNL), usually expressed as L_{eq} and is shown in Figure 6.1 where a fluctuating sound level is plotted against time. L_{eq} is usually taken for a nominal 8 h. Other terms having the same meaning as L_{eq} are sometimes used, such as $L_{EP, d}$, in which the d indicates daily.

Equivalent Continuous Sound Level

A simpler example is shown in Figure 6.2 in which a noise pattern is plotted which includes 114 dB (A) for 10 min, 105 dB (A) for 45 min and 92 db (A) for the remainder of the 8-h day. The equivalent continuous sound level comes out to be 100 dB (A). In other words the effect of the sound energy actually entering the operator's ear during the 8-h was equivalent to a continuous level of 100 dB (A). This is higher than one might have guessed by just looking at the noise pattern and is due to the higher levels having a greater influence than might be expected, due to the logarithmic vertical scale. The same effect is seen in Figure 6.1.

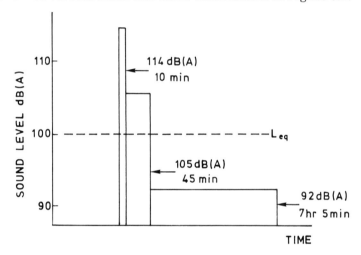

FIG. 6.2 Example showing $L_{eq\,(8)}$

L_{eq} can be calculated directly from the known pattern of noise exposure or the task left to an integrating sound level meter. A typical calculation, to show the principles involved, will be done later. When measured over the usual 8-h period, L_{eq} may be written as $L_{eq\,(8)}$.

A daily noise dose using $L_{eq\,(8)}$ now needs to be chosen so that a certain percentage of the exposed population will not suffer unacceptable hearing loss after a working lifetime, including age effects. Clearly the value chosen depends on the percentage to be protected and what is regarded as an unacceptable loss.

Available data suggest that a much greater reduction in the number of people at risk is gained by reducing $L_{eq\,(8)}$ from 100 dB (A) to 90 dB (A) than by reducing it from 90 dB (A) to 80 dB (A). This example of diminishing returns suggests that while most effort should be made to reduce levels below 90 dB (A), there remains some benefit from reducing levels still further. Such noise reduction costs a great deal of money and legislation is limited by what is reasonably practical, a phrase which is likely to be increasingly tested in the courts.

Not surprisingly, there are different national ideas on the desired value for $L_{eq(8)}$. The various accepted values are based on estimates of the sound levels at various frequencies that could provide a hazard to hearing for 8 h exposure daily over a working life. One set of data produced an overall level of 88 dB (A), which optimists rounded up to 90 dB (A) and pessimists lowed to 85 dB(A). Later optimists have since tended to overlook the fact that 90 dB (A) was regarded as an absolute upper limit for continuous steady daily noise without hearing protection and not a recommended level; the latter would preferably not exceed 85 dB (A).

National standards

The legal status, as well as the numerical values for L_{eq} in the work-place, varies from nation to nation and with time. At the time of writing, the only current statutory requirements in the United Kingdom cover woodworkers and agricultural tractor drivers. The 1972 'Code of Practice for Employed Persons' published by the United Kingdom Health and Safety Executive allows 90 dB (A) for $L_{eq(8)}$ and this level is currently specified by the British Army. A forthcoming United Kingdom Defence Standard is likely to recommend 85 dB (A). The lower 85 dB (A) is used already by the RAF.

However, a Council of the European Community (CEC) Directive of 1986, which requires implementation by member nations by 1990, specifies that:

▶ $L_{EP,d}$ (i.e. $L_{eq(8)}$) at the ear shall not exceed 90 dB (A).
▶ If $L_{EP,d}$ exceeds 85 dB (A), hearing protection shall be made available, although there is no requirement for workers to use it.
▶ If the peak (maximum instantaneous) pressure exceeds 140 dB (200 pascal), hearing protection shall be used, irrespective of the value of $L_{EP,d}$.

It is probable that, at some date in the future, the maximum $L_{EP,d}$ at the ear will be reduced to 85 dB (A).

An obvious question now is to what extent military and civilian criteria are compatible. There are clearly situations where some military requirement is paramount and questions of noise levels and the use of hearing protection have to go by the board. The training situation is another matter and the weapon noise criterion, for instance, recognises a preferred exposure and a maximum exposure without hearing protection. The typical military environment also, however, includes a civilian workforce looking to the appropriate Health and Safety at Work legislation and general noise standards for protection.

Legal aspects

The legal aspects of noise-induced hearing loss are relevant to those serving in Forces which do not have immunity to prosecution, as is now the case in the United Kingdom. The case of personnel deafened by an explosion is similar to any other sudden traumatic industrial injury. For the claim to hold, it is necessary to establish precisely what happened at the time and to show that what happened had a medically verifiable effect on the hearing of the claimant. It is then necessary to show that the employer was negligent and legally to blame. This all sounds relatively straightforward in an environment where hearing acuity is tested regularly and records are properly maintained. In real life, however, these latter two conditions may not be satisfied. In general, should immediate pre- and post-event audiograms not be available, it is not possible merely from measurements of sound levels on nominally identical sources to predict that damage would have occurred to a particular set of ears, given the wide variation in the sensitivity of ears.

Establishing the cause of long-term deafness is much more difficult. The present state of an individual's hearing is an indication of damage sustained over many years including many activities which are aurally hazardous. Some of these may have involved mandatory hearing protection which may not have been worn, or which might have been inappropriate or not functioning satisfactorily. Part of the hearing loss would be due to ageing and possibly disease.

Normally the claim will be made under Common Law, and it is necessary to establish negligence. As an alternative, in certain industries in the United Kingdom, it is possible to claim under the National Insurance industrial injuries scheme.

Trading intensity and time

The noise dose idea raises the possibility of using different combinations of spoon-size and spoons-per-day to produce the same total dose. For example, we might double the sound intensity (I) and halve the time allowed, thus keeping the total energy constant. We can do a direct dB calculation to compare $2I$ and I:

$$\text{for energy doubling, } 10 \log \frac{2I}{I} = 3 \text{ dB}$$

Starting with 90 dB (A) for 8 h, we could thus have 93 dB (A) for 4 h, 96 dB (A) for 2 h . . . 123 dB (A) for 15 s. Each exposure would have the same energy content. This all seems very straightforward but this bureaucratic neatness conceals some problems.

First, 123 dB (A) is typically found during a high-speed power-pack test; could we really be sure that the operator gives up after 15 s? Do we believe the 123 dB (A) figure and that ominous word 'typical'? In this context typical may really mean that 123 dB (A) was measured at one location on one occasion. As the operator moves around an engine, which will usually have a highly directional sound pattern and which will vary from day to day, that 123 dB (A) could really mean 123 ± 3 dB (A). The allowed exposure time now covers a range from 30 s to 7.5 s.

Secondly, the United States does not at present accept the 3 dB (A) trade-off for doubling or halving exposure times but uses 5 dB (A) instead. The differences in allowed exposure time can be considerable; for example, 102 dB (A) is allowed for 30 min on the 90 dB (A)/3 dB (A) trade-off scale but 91 min on the 5 dB (A) version. The most stringent 85 dB (A)/3 dB (A) trade-off cuts this to 9.5 min. The data available on the relation between noise exposure and hearing loss are insufficient to determine which, if either, of the 3 dB (A) and 5 dB (A) trade-offs is correct. Extrapolating the 5 dB (A) trade-off to very short durations is clearly not advisable.

Calculating L_{eq}

Basically, all an integrating sound level meter does is to add the various contributions to the total dose, i.e. the dB (A) × time for each, during the working day of 8 h. If it then divides by 8 h or 480 min, depending on the unit that durations are being mesured in, it gets the constant dB (A) level giving the same total dose.

The only problem is that dB (A)s are in log form and time is not. They must both be in the same form so an easy approach is to:

▶ Divide the duration by 8 (if it is in hours) or 480 (if it is in minutes).
▶ Find the logarithm (base 10) of this and multiply by 10.
▶ Add it to the measured sound level in dB (A).

For instance, if the noise exposure is 93 dB (A) for 4 h, we proceed as follows:

▶ 4 h divided by 8 h = 0.5

log 0.5 = −0.3 (approx.)

▶ ∴ 10 log 0.5 = −3
▶ 93 dB (A) + (−3)= 90 dB (A)

confirming the early statement that 93 dB (A) for 4 h is equivalent to 90 dB (A) for 8 h.

This calculation has followed European practice is using the 3 dB (A) trade-off. Current United States practice would allow 95 dB (A) over 4 h.

Again, 108 dB for 15 min is dealt with as follows:

▶ 15 min divided by 480 min = 0.031
▶ log 0.031 = −1.5 (approx.)
▶ 10 log 0.031 = −15
▶ 108 dB (A) + (−15) = 93 dB (A)

and this is above the usual criteria for $L_{eq\,(8)}$

Where exposure is to more than one level, we just sum the exposures according to the normal rules for adding levels in dB (see Chapter 3). For instance, if the daily exposure included both above exposures the total L_{Eq} would be:

$$90 \text{ dB (A)} + 93 \text{ dB (A)} = 95 \text{ dB (A) (approx.)}$$

Example 1

Figure 6.2 shows the pattern of 114 dB (A) for 10 min, 105 dB (A) for 45 min and 92 dB (A) for 425 min. Dividing the durations by 480 and adding the 10 log of these to the respective sound levels gives the three contributions as 114 − 16.8 = 97 dB (A), 105 − 10.2 = 95 dB (A) and 92 − 0.5 = 91.5 dB (A). Adding these yields an $L_{eq\,(8)}$ of 100 dB (A), as indicated in the Figure.

Example 2

A more complicated example comes from data obtained during a 50-min flight on the cargo deck of a Hercules transport aircraft which included a practice landing with immediate rolling take-off. The aircraft was unloaded and the engine did not

dB (A)	Number of samples	dB(A)	Number of samples
≤80	0	94	475
82	18	96	122
84	254	98	68
86	3845	100	19
88	7384	102	33
90	1928	104	8
92	1084	≥106	0

exceed 60% power on level flight. A statistical sound level meter was used to sample and record the sound level every 0.2 s and store it in a memory. Subsequent analysis showed how the number of samples varied between different dB (A) levels:

The value of L_{eq} calculated by the meter was 90 dB (A), closer to the average sound level 88.5 dB (A) than in the previous example due to the relative lack of peaks in the sound pattern.

British Standard (BS) 5330 provides a table, based on such calculations.

> *But many military tasks, such as a helicopter pilot, have a limited period authorised per week, rather than per day. Can the noise exposure be averaged over the whole week?*

In principle we can use the same procedure but work in terms of the fraction of a 40 h week that is actual exposure time. Alternatively, we can just find the average fraction of daily exposure and use exactly the same calculation.

For example, assume a Wessex helicopter pilot is allowed to fly for 8½ h per week and that the sound level at his seat is 104 dB (A). For a 5 day week, his daily exposure time is 8.5/5 or 1.7 h and the steps in the calculation become:

▶ 1.7 h divided by 8 h = 0.21.

▶ $10 \log 0.21 = -6.7$.

▶ 104 dB (A) + (−6.7) = 97 dB (A).

This would be well above an 85 dB (A) limit but it has neglected the reduction in sound level due to his helmet. This has to be 12 dB (A) to reduce $L_{eq\,(8)}$ at the ear to 85 dB (A).

Opinions (and standards) are divided over whether such a calculation is permissible; if the bulk of the 8½ h occurred on a single day, averaging over a whole week is definitely not recommended. A safer alternative would be to evaluate the greatest exposure which is likely to occur on any one day.

It should also be remembered that exposures from many different sources will probably occur during the course of a whole week, and a calculation of total noise dose should include them all.

Noise dosemeters

The next stage from an instrument which directly measures L_{eq} over a given period is one which gives a read-out directly as a percentage of the allowed dose. To do this it needs two pieces of information: the local 100% figure for 8 h (85 or 90 dB (A)), and how to trade off time and dB (A), i.e. is it 3 or 5 dB (A) for halving/doubling time? The manufacturer will build the meter for certain combinations of these; the user must beware that the instrument being used conforms to local practice. Some dosemeters ignore levels below 80 dB (A) since such levels are insignificant on the 90 dB (A) criterion (Figure 3.3); they would not be insignificant on the 85 dB (A) criterion.

The dosemeter (Figure 6.3) is a small instrument, the meter being placed in a breast pocket and the attached microphone positioned as close as possible to the ear, e.g. clipped to a safety helmet (Figure 6.4). Attaching the microphone to the overalls can give a high reading due to reflections from the body. High readings also result if users blow into them or shout into them, a common practice partly to see if they work and partly as a game. Accidental touching or knocking can yield spuriously high figures.

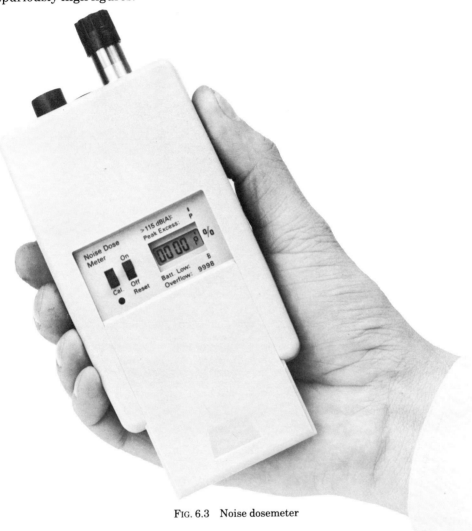

FIG. 6.3 Noise dosemeter

The current position

It has generally been agreed that the hazard to hearing can be expressed in terms of a continuous equivalent sound level $L_{eq(8)}$, replacing the actual varying noise pattern during an 8 h working day. The allowed value of $L_{eq(8)}$ for hearing conservation purposes varies but it is likely that 85 dB (A) will be a standard value some time in the future. It is certainly a figure to aim for.

Weapon noise has been excluded from the discussion so far as rather different criteria are used. It is considered in Chapter 7.

FIG. 6.4   Use of a noise dosemeter

SELF TEST QUESTIONS

Question 1   Assuming the 85 dB (A) 8 h limit and a 3 dB (A) allowed increase for halving exposure time, estimate the allowed unprotected exposure time for a level of 103 dB (A).

Answer ....

....

....

Question 2   Calculate the exposure time at 110 dB (A) equivalent to 85 dB (A) for 8 h.

Answer ....

....

....

Question 3   The sound level inside an office close to a pre-flight check area is 104 dB (A) on six occasions during an 8 h day, each exposure lasting 5 min. Throughout the rest of the day the sound level remains at 75 dB (A). Calculate the effective $L_{eq\,(8)}$.

Answer ....

....

....

Question 4   Find the total $L_{eq\,(8)}$ for 6 h at 88 dB (A) and 2 h at 98 dB (A).

Answer ....

....

....

Question 5   One of the ground crew carrying out a pre-flight check on a Jaguar aircraft was exposed to 126 dB (A) for 2 min and 108 dB (A) for 3 min close to the aircraft, and 100 dB (A) for 5 min while watching from a position 1 m from a ground power unit. His muffs produced an effective sound level reduction of only 15 dB (A) due to hurried fitting and they were worn only for the two exposures close to the aircraft. Was this total exposure over the 85 dB (A) 8 h limit? Would his moving away from the GPU have helped significantly to reduce the received dose?

Answer ....

....

....

Answers on page 114.

7. Weapon Noise

The acoustic pressure wave, or pulse, radiated from a weapon or explosion differs in several significant respects from the waves considered in Chapter 2. These differences affect the response of the ear, the criteria for hearing hazard and the measurement technique used. For these reasons there has been no mention so far of weapon noise, which is now discussed.

Impulse Noise

In a military context, impulse noise usually results from an explosion, as in gunfire, although some industrial processes such as drop forging can also produce a type of impulse noise. The term impulse is rather loosely defined, but implies both a very high maximum pressure and a very short duration. Impulse noise from explosive sources is sometimes loosely described as blast.

Since the pressures involved are comparable to atmospheric pressure, the normal laws of acoustics, which assume that the acoustic pressures are much less than atmospheric pressure, do not always apply. One consequence of this is the formation of a shock wave, travelling supersonically, wherever a substantial increase in pressure occurs.

If a microphone is placed a few metres distant from a small spherical explosive charge in free air, the measured change in pressure with time is as shown in Figure 7.1.

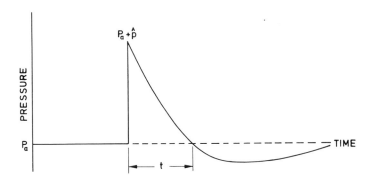

Fig. 7.1   Idealised impulse noise

The shock wave travels outward from the source; the pressure ahead of the shock front is the ambient (atmospheric) pressure p_a, and immediately behind is $(p_a + \hat{p})$

where $\hat{p}$ is the peak pressure, sometimes referred to as overpressure. The pressure then decays until, at a time t after the arrival of the shock front, the pressure is again equal to atmospheric pressure. The pressure then falls further to below atmospheric pressure, before it eventually returns to atmospheric pressure.

In the area where crew are likely to be stationed, $\hat{p}$ will generally be less than atmospheric, and both $\hat{p}$ and t are proportional to the one-third power of the energy of the charge for a constant distance from the charge. Very close to the source, the variation of pressure with time is much more complicated; however this should not affect the design of equipment since people should not be in this area! Further away, outside the normal crew positions, the shock front decays and becomes a more gradual rise. This is due partly to atmospheric turbulence and partly to the absorption of high frequencies by air. Its propagation also becomes affected by weather conditions.

For a more detailed description of the generation of impulse noise from guns see *Military Ballistics — A Basic Manual* in this series; this provides Figure 7.2, showing the shock front from a 5.56 mm rifle muzzle.

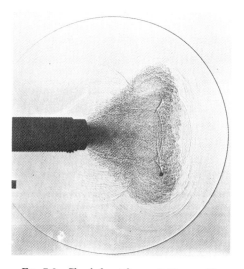

FIG. 7.2   Shock front from a 5.56 mm rifle

In practice, the pressure/time relation is complicated by reflections from adjacent objects, including the ground, and in some cases by secondary sources as well. In the case of recoilless guns, such as 84 mm Carl Gustav, both the muzzle and venturi act as sources. The simple pattern of Figure 7.1 is thus an exception rather than a rule. Figure 7.3 shows the effect of a ground reflection. Close to the ground, there is a tendency for the direct and reflected shocks to coalesce.

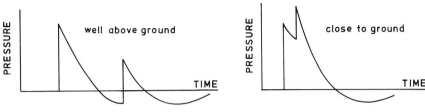

FIG. 7.3   Impulse noise outdoors

Where many reflecting surfaces exist, for instance with a gun fired inside a room, the pattern of reflections becomes very complicated, and the peak pressure direct from the source may be much less than from some of the reflections. Figure 7.4 compares the first part of the pressure traces from a 5.56 mm rifle in an indoor range (a) 2 m to one side of the muzzle and (b) 2 m behind the muzzle. In (a) the sources of the various peaks are indicated; in (b) the direct pressure wave is much smaller than the following reverberant sound. (Note the different scales for the plots.)

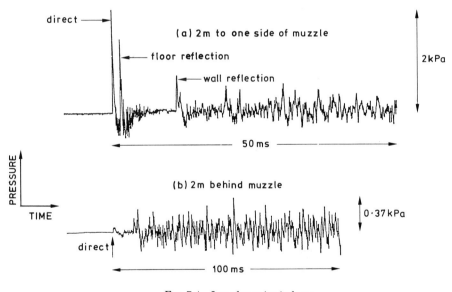

FIG. 7.4   Impulse noise indoors

Sources can be highly directional; for instance, with a gun, the greatest pressures are in front of the muzzle. Figure 7.5 shows the distribution of the peak pressure around a 7.62 mm rifle. In this case, strictly speaking, the source is the slug of expanding gas travelling forward of the muzzle, rather than the muzzle itself. However, if the gun has a muzzle brake, the pressures may be greatest behind the muzzle, in the crew positions.

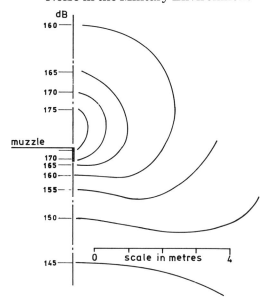

FIG. 7.5   Peak pressure contours around a 7.62 mm rifle

Measurement of Impulse Noise

This discussion has emphasised one major difference between the measurement of impulse noise and the measurement of continuous noise. Since impulse noise is of short duration, it is possible to represent its entire pressure history, for example as a trace giving pressure as a function of time. Such a record can give valuable information about the way in which the noise is propagated. It can also give some indication of the validity of the results! It is a good rule that reports of impulse noise measurement should always show representative pressure histories.

All current criteria for assessing impulse noise make use of the peak pressure $\hat{p}$, so it is vital that this quantity is measured accurately. Other quantities which have been used are the duration of the noise and its energy (linear or A-weighted). It may also be useful to provide an analysis of frequency content.

In principle, measurement of impulse noise is not more difficult than measurement of continuous noise; but there are a number of traps for the unwary. As a general rule, equipment designed for the measurement of continuous noise is rarely suitable for impulse noise. The authors have seen too many instances where use of unsuitable equipment has given meaningless or even misleading results. In particular, conventional sound level meters are quite unsuitable; the time over which they average, to produce a rms answer, is much longer than the duration of a typical weapon noise, The pre- and post-firing 'silences' are included in the averaging and give an answer that is too low. Peak pressures and rms pressures are also no longer simply related; in fact p_{rms} cannot strictly be defined for a short-duration impulse. The microphones are also unlikely to respond adequately to the high sound levels present.

The first requirement is that microphones and their preamplifiers must function at the pressures being measured, and that calibration procedures must cover this range. The most commonly used microphones, which are also known as pressure transducers or blast gauges, are:

▶ Miniature capacitance microphones, generally of nominal ¼″ (6 mm) or ⅛″ (3 mm) external diameter. These are excellent for the measurement of small-arms noise, but unsuitable for the greater pressures close to heavy weapons.

▶ Piezo-resistive microphones, which have a strain gauge mounted on the rear surface of a diaphragm to monitor its movement. Only the smallest sizes are suitable, since the resonant frequency of the diaphragm must be very high if the measurements are not to be affected.

▶ Piezo-electric pressure transducers. In these the pressure applied directly to the sensitive element produces an electrical charge. These transducers are most accurate and reliable when the element is made of quartz; other materials are more sensitive but tend to respond to changes in temperature. Piezo-electric transducers are robust and well suited to the measurement of high pressures, but must be mounted with special care since they also respond to vibration. The coaxial cable between the transducer and amplifier must be of a low-noise type and be positioned so that it does not move; cable movement can also give a small charge output which can be confused with the signal from the transducer.

▶ Foil gauges, in which the bursting of a thin metal foil placed over apertures of various diameter gives an indication of the peak pressure. They are useful but give no information on duration.

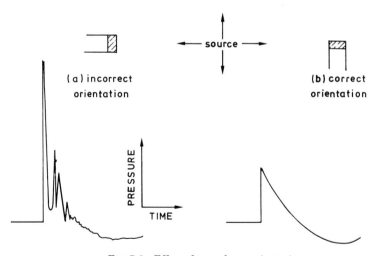

FIG. 7.6   Effect of transducer orientation

The orientation of the sensitive surface of the transducer is critical. If the shock wave strikes the surface end-on and is reflected, the pressure increase due to the reflection will give an exaggerated value for peak pressure (Figure 7.6). This may also excite any resonances the transducer may have, giving an entirely spurious value for the peak pressure. Figure 7.6 also shows the correct orientation. In such a case however, the measured pressure will show a slower rise time, which is equivalent to the transit time of the shock across the transducer surface. This can be alleviated by making the transducer surface as small as possible.

At the higher pressures, above approximately 7 kPa (roughly 1 psi), turbulence around the body of the transducer will give an inaccurate value for duration. This can be avoided by the use of a streamlined baffle. If the baffle is circular, the transducer will measure noise from any source, or reflection, in the plane of the baffle. Figure 7.7 shows the correct alignment. Misalignment of the baffle will give large errors which can be reduced by the use of two sensitive surfaces, one each side of the baffle.

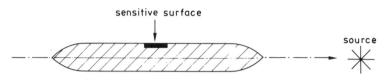

FIG. 7.7   Orientation of transducer with baffle

Measurements should normally be made with the human being absent, and with transducers at the position normally occupied by the head. Where a very complex pattern of reflections is expected, an instrumented dummy with transducers at the ear positions may be useful.

The recording system must give a flat frequency response to at least 40 kHz. Originally, the transducer output was captured photographically, for instance on an oscilloscope screen. This gave an excellent trace of the waveform, but subsequent analysis of (for instance) frequency content was not possible. More recently, FM instrumentation tape recorders have been used. Care should be taken to avoid both over-recording, which will clip the peak, and under-recording, which will leave the signal buried in tape-recorder noise. Direct recording hi-fi machines are not suitable.

Digital storage of the signal is becoming increasingly attractive. The time between samples should be as short as possible; 5 microseconds is suggested.

A calibration check of all equipment is required on-site, preferably before and after measurement. An electromechanical high-level calibrator giving pressures of a few kPa is convenient.

Measurement of impulse noise is subject to the universal law that 'if something can go wrong, it will'. Results from one round should be examined before the next is fired, and plenty of time should be allowed. It is helpful to allocate extra rounds for setting up the equipment.

Guidelines for the measurement of impulse noise from weapons are given in Appendix 1 of NATO Document AC/243 (Panel 8 / RSG 6) D/9 'Effects of Impulse Noise'.

Human response to impulse noise

The main effect of impulse noise on the ear is to produce a high-frequency hearing loss. This is very similar to the loss from continuous noise and is due to damage to the nerve cells in the cochlea. There is a very large variation in individual sensitivity — even greater than with continuous noise — so that one individual may be unaffected by an exposure which leaves his comrade with a substantial hearing loss. It is possible for intense exposure to produce mechanical disruption within the cochlea, so that substantial hearing loss can occur after just one impulse ('acoustic trauma').

At relatively high pressures, other effects can occur, especially where the duration is increased by reverberation or by relatively large charge weights.

Ear drum rupture has been reported at 50 – 56 kPa (7 – 8 psi), measured at the ear drum, when the duration of the positive phase of the impulse exceeds 2ms. This pressure at the ear drum can be produced by pressures as low as 15 kPa (2 psi), measured in free-field away from reflecting surfaces, if the pressure is reflected from the side of the head. This injury will not usually, of itself, produce total deafness, and can sometimes heal spontaneously.

At peak pressures around 100 kPa (1 atm or 15 psi), injury can occur to gas-containing organs (lungs and intestines), resulting in haemorrhage. The threshold for lethal injuries is about 270 kPa (40 psi). With peak pressures of 500 – 700 kPa (70 – 100 psi), lethal injuries will be induced in about 50% of those exposed, although this will also depend on duration. The effect will be greater with multiple exposures or exposures in confined spaces. Normally, with such pressures, there is an even greater hazard from fragments or collapsing masonry.

Limits to impulse noise exposure

It is more difficult to draw up exposure limits for weapon noise than for continuous industrial-type noise due to the lack of well-documented data. Available data on permanent hearing loss in military personnel at the end of their service is fragmentary and an individual's noise exposure history can rarely be identified. It has been necessary to fall back on data from temporary threshold shifts due to known sources, much of which involved rifles alone.

The majority of such limits have involved three quantities:
   ▶ The peak pressure $\hat{p}$.
   ▶ The number of impulses.
   ▶ The duration of each impulse.

In some cases the orientation of the head has also been considered, since the pressure at the ear closest to the source is increased by reflection at the side of the head. This increase does not, of course, occur if the subject is looking directly towards or away from the source. In practice, head orientation is difficult to define.

The duration of an impulse can be defined in several different ways. The studies, conducted in the mid-1960s, which eventually led to the current limits for both United States and United Kingdom usage, defined two durations, the A- and B-durations. The A-duration was to be used in the simple case shown in Figure 7.1, where it has the value t; the B-duration was to be used wherever any reflection, reverberation or secondary sources were present. In practice, there is always some reflection, even if only from the ground, so that the B-duration, which yields the greater estimate of hazard, is used. Figure 7.8, taken from the United Kingdom Defence Standard 00-27/1 (1986) shows the means of estimating B-duration (simply referred to as 'duration' in that standard). It is simply the total time during which the envelope of the pressure fluctuations is within one-tenth of the peak pressure. In dB terms, this means comparing $\hat{p}/10$ with $\hat{p}$ using:

$$20 \log \frac{\hat{p}/10}{\hat{p}} \text{, giving a 20 dB reduction from the peak pressure.}$$

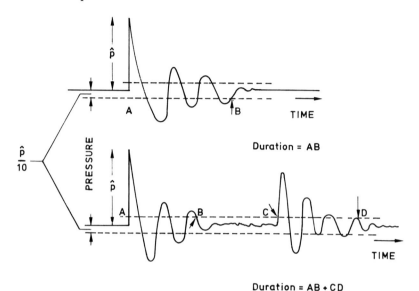

FIG. 7.8   Definition of B-duration

The upper line of Figure 7.9 shows the maximum allowed combinations of peak pressure and duration given in this Defence Standard. This line assumed 100 firings per day on an occasional basis.

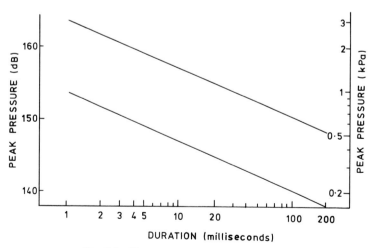

FIG. 7.9   Maximum impulse noise exposure

This standard also prescribes the lower, preferred, limit shown, approximately 10 dB lower where a very low risk of noise-induced hearing loss is required. An allowance of 20 or 25 dB (depending on type) is permitted where hearing protection is used.

Both curves of Figure 7.9 can be shifted vertically to allow for other than 100 impulses per day. Figure 7.10 gives the corrections to be applied.

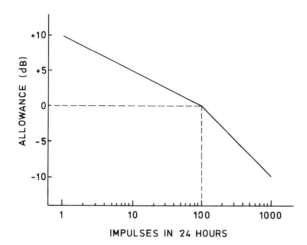

FIG. 7.10   Allowance for number of exposures

The United States Army MIL-STD-1474 B 'Noise Limits for Army Materiel' follows a somewhat similar approach; the only major difference is a limit of 140 dB (0.2 kPa), irrespective of number or duration of impulses, where no hearing protection is being used. This requirement, which is not strictly justified on purely technical grounds, is intended to enforce the use of hearing protection on all occasions of exposure.

A quite different approach is used in current French standards. The A-weighted energy (in terms of L_{eq}) of the impulse is used, in much the same way as the A-weighted energy of continuous noise. There is also a limit to the peak pressure of the unprotected ear. Limits of 85 dB (A) for $L_{eq\,(8)}$, and 160 dB (2 kPa) for peak pressure, were originally proposed; however, a limit of 90 dB (A) for $L_{eq\,(8)}$ was eventually adopted. Although this approach seems quite different to one based on peak pressure and duration, the limits in practical use are remarkably similar.

In the long term, there is a possibility of improved standards based on mathematical models of the ear's functioning and on animal studies; it is not yet possible to say what form the improved standards might take.

Typical impulse noise exposures

Table 7.1 gives a rough guide to the peak pressure to be expected from various impulse noise exposures.

TABLE 7.1   TYPICAL PEAK PRESSURE FOR WEAPONS

Peak Pressure		Example
kPa	dB	
200	200	Thunderflash in slit trench or vehicle
100	194	(1 atm)
50	188	84 mm medium anti-armour weapon (MAW) Medium mortar, maximum charge, crew positions
20	180	Towed howitzer, maximum charge, crew positions
10	174	Medium howitzer shell burst at 50 m
5	168	Service rifle, 1 m to side of muzzle
2	160	Service rifle (7.62 mm or 5.56 mm) at firer's ear
1	154	Tank gun, measured inside closed-down tank
0.2	140	0.22″ rim-fire target rifle

B-durations are generally longer with larger calibre weapons and are greatly extended by reflection or reverberation. For instance, at the firer's ear, the B-duration from a rifle is about 5 ms, but from a medium howitzer is about 40 ms, a light howitzer ~ 25 ms, a mortar ~ 15 ms, a live rifle round in an indoor range ~ 150 ms, and a tank gun measured inside a tank ~ 200 ms.

It is worth noting that the greater risk to hearing comes from a soldier's own weapons rather than from the efforts of the opposition. The greatest risk of all, at least during normal peacetime training, comes not from a weapon but from a simple training device, the thunderflash. It is quite common, despite regulations to the contrary, for these devices to be thrown or dropped into slit trenches or vehicles. One thunderflash can easily cause a hearing loss incompatible with further military service.

Example

Figure 7.11 shows the layout of a trench used for thunderflash and 7.62 mm rifle blank measurements by APRE. With the latter, the blank firing adaptor, which reduces noise as well as allowing automatic operation of the rifle, was not used.

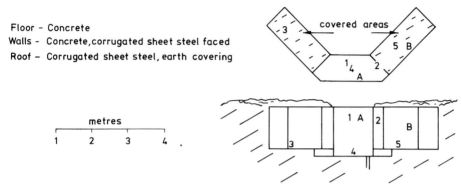

Floor – Concrete
Walls – Concrete, corrugated sheet steel faced
Roof – Corrugated sheet steel, earth covering

FIG. 7.11   Trench layout

Typical data at the measuring positions A and B shown here were:

	Source position	Measurement position	Peak pressure (dB)	B-duration (ms)
7.66 mm	1	A	184.0	17
Rifle		B	161.1	78
	2	A	165.9	53
		B	165.7	48
Thunderflash	3	A	182.1	100
		B	181	100
	4	A	201.1	15
		B	184.5	50
	5	A	165.8	17.5
		B	191.4	50

Summary

Weapon noise requires a specialised measurement technique. The method of evaluating the risk to hearing also differs from that used with continuous noise; current standards use the peak pressure and duration of the impulse. Indoor firings extend the duration and may also increase the peak pressure, and therefore pose a particularly severe risk to hearing.

SELF TEST QUESTIONS

Question 1   The noise from a rifle is measured 1 m to the side of the muzzle; the peak pressure is 8 kPa and the duration is 3 ms. If, during a field firing exercise, the rifle is fired with another rifleman's head in this position, how many rounds can be fired before the risk to his hearing becomes excessive? (Assume hearing protection is not used.)

Answer ....

....

....

Question 2   (a)   A light howitzer gives, at the layer's position, a peak pressure of 20 kPa (180 dB) and a duration of 20 ms. It is proposed to fire a maximum of 10 rounds/day during normal training. Is this permissible and, if so, what precautions are required to prevent hearing loss?

(b)   Due to instability in the gun, the use of a muzzle brake is proposed. This will increase the peak pressure by a factor of approximately 3, the duration remaining approximately constant. Is the gun then safe for manned firing?

Answer ....

....

....

Question 3   The peak pressure from a blank rifle round, measured at the firer's ear, is 0.6 kPa (150 dB) with a duration of 3 ms when the rifle is fired outdoors with a blank firing adaptor. When fired indoors, during training for combat in built-up areas, the peak pressure is increased to 2 kPa (160 dB) and the duration is increased to 150 ms. What are the likely risks to hearing in the two circumstances, and what precautions need to be taken to protect hearing?

Answer ....

....

....

Answers on page 115.

8. Noise in Workshops and Maintenance Areas

The Problem

Figure 8.1 shows a vehicle maintenance area which involves most of the problems to be faced in this chapter. The main area A accommodates a range of vehicles, wheeled and tracked, and is open-plan with brick walls and a large sliding access door at B which is generally left open except in winter. There are offices opposite this door, 10 m away, with their only windows facing the door. Area A itself has single glazed windows along most of the upper third of walls C and D. E is a small cell with breeze-block walls and concrete roof and a pair of wooden sliding doors at F which leave a gap of over 2 cm on either side when shut. This cell houses a main battle tank power pack for run-up tests. A small office G is of block walls with a non-openable window and an ill-fitting door which is generally left open in the summer.

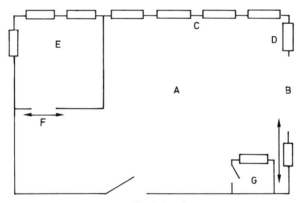

Fig. 8.1   Workshop layout

The noise-producing activities here range from engine-running to rivetting. The result will be a definite hazard to hearing in cell E and possibly just outside it, hazards close to other running vehicles and annoyance to the occupants of the various offices. Vehicle movements to and from the workshop may also cause hazard and annoyance. The noise problem has been broadened to include both annoyance and the effect of noise on tasks requiring concentration.

The construction and relative position of buildings on military stations often takes little account of present day noise levels. Many were built before noise legislation came in, at a time when noise was regarded as an inevitable part of the job, and when vehicle engines, for example, were far quieter. Since then, parts of the buildings may have been used to house intense noise sources giving up to 125 dB (A) close by, as was cell E in the above example. Complete buildings may have been put to new uses which are ill-adapted to their lightweight construction. One example is a hangar with a flimsy roof in which radar equipment is maintained, requiring careful electronic measurement, and which is placed under a Tornado take-off path. Any hearing conservation programme must, as well as identifying existing hazardous areas, recognise the likely emergence of new ones as intense noise sources are added or relocated.

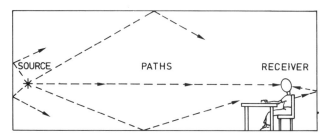

FIG. 8.2   Sound paths in an enclosure

When discussing indoor noise we have to include the whole acoustic system of source, receiver and the paths taken by the sound (Figure 8.2). The usual line of argument is basically to see whether the received noise level is high enough to create a hazard or to interfere with the task in hand to a significant degree. This requires a systematic noise survey of the workshop, of how the sound level varies from place to place with all the usual machines running and with each machine and noisy process measured separately. The worst offenders can then be identified and hopefully modified or screened as they may affect the sound level throughout the whole area. The criterion is to get below an $L_{eq(8)}$ of 85 dB (A) or 90 dB (A) to prevent damage; the maximum noise levels to prevent annoyance are discussed later in this Chapter.

On a day-to-day basis this is idealistic. The positioning of the main noise sources in, say, a maintenance area for vehicles or aircraft will vary from day to day as work processes and their positions will be restricted by the space available. On at least one airfield, safety dictates that Tornado aircraft be placed so that their engines point into a busy hangar. Trained personnel and equipment are not available for frequent noise surveys and the best that can be done might realistically be the segregation of noisiest tasks into an area that is acoustically treated and in which personnel are required to spend only essential time. The need-to-shout-at-one-metre test can be useful in identifying troublesome sources.

Reduction of sound levels at source or the modification of the path taken by the sound are recommendations which follow a noise survey. These cost money. The simplest and cost-effective answer of moving the receiver must not be overlooked. The working pattern of an individual around a running engine should be examined to minimise the time spent close to the source, even with hearing protection being worn. Unit hearing conservation programmes (if they exist!) should ensure that personnel at risk are fully aware of the need to reduce exposure and to discipline themselves. Groups of individuals performing such a task should be familiar enough with the procedure to avoid the need to bellow into an ear from which protection has been removed, as has been seen ten feet from a jet engine on full power!

Sound in Enclosures

Inside the enclosure we first have sound coming directly from a source without reflections en route. This direct sound spreads out as discussed in Chapter 2; for an effective point source the resulting intensity I depends on $1/r^2$ at a distance r, giving a reduction of four times on doubling distance. Translating this into dB, we compare:

$$I \text{ to } I/4 \text{ by } 10 \log \frac{I/4}{I},$$

suggesting that the direct sound should fall by 6 dB on every doubling of distance.

This is easily tested by using a small source; recall that large sources can give a spread of sound levels close up due to interference. Figure 8.3 shows how the level in dB changed with the distance from a power drill, a source which can be hazardous when operated close to the ear for too long. The lower plot was obtained in a 'dead' (anechoic) room treated to markedly reduce any reflections and we find a decrease of about 6 dB on doubling distance.

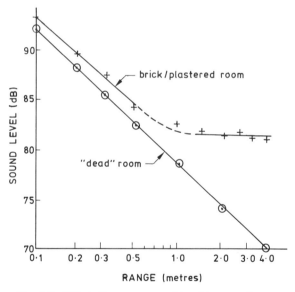

FIG. 8.3   Effect of range on sound level in an enclosure

The upper plot of Figure 8.3 is for a 'live' room with plastered brick walls; something odd happens beyond 0.5 m — the sound level gradually becomes unchanging with distance. The culprits are the room surfaces which have reflected the sound to produce so-called reverberant sound, travelling all round the room and adding to the direct sound.

The direct sound dominates close to the source and the reverberant sound well away from it. So the basic questions to be asked are: first, for whom am I trying to

reduce the noise level, and, second, is he in the region where the direct or reverberant sound is dominant? Reducing the reverberant field will do little for a mechanic
working on the engine in the dedicated test cell; on the other hand, in a workshop
area he would also be exposed to reverberant sound from other sources.

Sound Absorption

We reduce the reverberant sound by covering the surface with materials which
will not reflect sound, called absorbers. These are generally porous materials having narrow channels into which the pressure waves can penetrate and hopefully
lose energy by friction. The ability to absorb is measured as the fraction of the incident energy that is absorbed (i.e. not reflected) called the absorption coefficient.

Notice that we say nothing about where the energy that is not reflected goes —
it could go straight on through the material (an open window has an absorption
coefficient of one, the maximum value) but it may be hard luck for the fellow next
door. This is the important difference between absorption and insulation of sound.
An absorber does not reflect but may allow sound through it, an insulator, such as
a brick wall, may reflect well but allow little sound through.

The choice of an absorber depends on the frequency range of the incident sound.
Porous materials cope quite well with higher frequencies but special arrangements
have to be made for low frequencies using resonance effects, as when blowing over
empty beer bottles. Absorbers on rigid walls should in theory be at least a quarter-
wavelength thick since it is at this distance from the wall that the incident and
reflected waves combine to give the vibrating air particles a maximum velocity and
hence a maximum frictional loss. But at low frequencies it would have to be inconveniently thick (80 cm at 100 Hz). Figure 8.4 shows the effect for a mineral wool

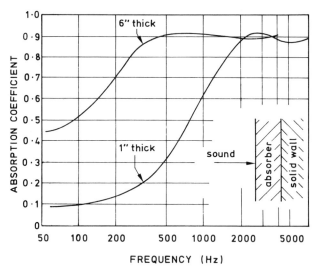

FIG. 8.4   Absorption by a mineral wool slab

slab. A better idea, then, is to just hang a thinner sheet of absorber at the distance
of $\lambda/4$ from the wall. Figure 8.5 shows the effect, with the peak absorption when
the frequency is such that the set distance from the wall becomes $\lambda/4$. This obviously works best for sound having this dominant wavelength.

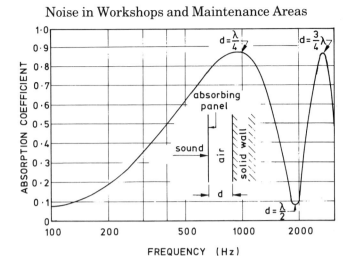

FIG. 8.5   Absorption by a suspended panel

A common solution for low frequencies is a panel with many holes which is separated from a wall by absorbent materials. The absorption obtained depends on the number of holes, their size, and the thickness of the backing. By selecting these quantities carefully we can obtain an absorber like that in Figure 8.6 which performs well around 125 to 250 Hz, a region where other forms of noise reduction, such as the use of hearing protection, are not always sufficiently effective. One practical problem with porous absorbers is that they can absorb oil and other contaminants, and so represent a possible fire risk.

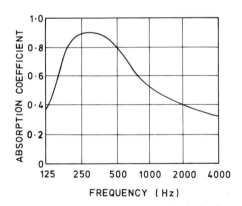

FIG. 8.6   Absorption of a perforated panel

But how much will the sound level fall due to the absorbers added to walls and ceiling?

Not at all close to a source, where direct sound dominates. Well away from the source the sound intensity is inversely proportional to the total absorption present. The total absorption is the sum of all the areas involved (in square metres) multiplied by their respective absorption coefficients. As an example, two absorption coefficients averaged over mid-to-high frequencies are: brick wall (painted) 0.02, mineral wool slabs on a rigid wall 0.8. If we start with a brick surface of area, say, 300 m^2 the initial absorption is 300 x 0.02 = 6 units; if we now increase its absorption coefficient from 00.02 to 0.8 by adding slabs, the final total absorption is 300 x 0.8 = 240 units. The ratio of sound intensities will be 6/240 = 0.025 and this means a dB change of 10 log 0.025 = – 16 dB. A useful rule of thumb is that doubling the absorption gives a 3 dB reduction.

Adding absorbers is thus most worthwhile when there are large reflecting surfaces which can be treated to increase the absorption by a large amount. Acoustic panels added to bare walls and ceiling of a moderately sized room can give a 10–15 dB drop in level. Suspended absorbent panels, which absorb on both sides, can achieve the same. It may be commented that a 10–15 dB drop seems to be little compensation for all the effort and cost. But a 10 dB drop means that the sound energy is reduced by a factor of 10, and a 15 dB drop by a factor of 30, allowing 10 times, or 30 times respectively, the exposure duration for the same dose. But if the initial sound level is 125 dB, a decrease to 115 dB, or 110 dB, is not enough.

This can all be applied to the mechanic working around the power pack in cell E in Figure 8.1. Far enough away from the engine, he will be in the reverberant sound field due to reflections from the painted brick walls, the bare concrete floor and the plastered ceiling. The cell is 8 m square and 5 m high with wooden sliding doors 3 m x 3 m and windows occupying a total area of 15 m^2. The engine on idle, and at full power for bursts of about 30 s, gave the following octave frequency spectra 3 m away:

Engine idling:

Centre Frequency (Hz)	31.5	63	125	250	500	1000	2000	4000	8000
Sound level (dB)	78	88	84	71	76	73	69	57	50

Engine on full power:

Centre Frequency (Hz)	31.5	63	125	250	500	1000	2000	4000	8000
Sound level (dB)	85	97	109	106	106	122	111	106	99

Notice the dominant low frequency sound on idle and the familiar high pitched whine on full power. The reader should be able immediately to put a figure on the dB (A) level in the full-power condition. 1000 Hz is dominant, so that the correction to dB (A) is zero and we have 122 dB (A). We now want a rough calculation of how much reduction in level we would get by adding mineral wool slabs to the brick areas and ceiling. First the geometry. The total wall area is 4 x 8 x 5 = 160 m^2 of which 15 m^2 is glass and 9 m^2 wooden door, giving 136 m^2 of brick. Ceiling and floor areas are 64 m². Oversimplifying, we assume that the average absorption coefficients are as follows, giving this absorption data:

Material	Abs. coeff.	Area (m²)	Area x abs. coeff.
Window	0.1	15	1.5
Brick (unpainted)	0.04	136	5.4
Plasterboard ceiling	0.1	64	6.4
Concrete floor	0.01	64	0.6
Wood	0.15	9	1.4

The total initial absorption is 15.3 units. Adding the mineral wool slabs to brick and ceiling increases the absorption column as follows:

Material	Abs. coeff.	Area (m²)	Area x abs. coeff.
Window	0.1	15	1.5
Brick + mineral wool	0.8	136	109
Ceiling + mineral wool	0.8	64	51
Concrete floor	0.01	64	0.6
Wood	0.15	9	1.4

to give a new absorption of 163.5 units.

The sound level changes by 10 log 15.3/163.5 or −10.3 dB. An array of 40 mineral wool panels hanging from the ceiling each 1 m x 0.6 m, would increase the total absorption by a further 1 x 0.6 x 0.8 x 80 = 38 units and the final reduction increases to 11 dB; the hanging panels would have been a waste of money. A more precise calculation would have to be done for each octave frequency band to take account of peaks in the initial spectrum.

Sound Insulation

The obvious next move is to try to reduce the power being radiated out by the engine by enclosing it or using barriers, in other words to insulate it. For good insulation we need to reduce greatly the sound level from one side of a wall (or panel) to the other. The Sound Reduction Index (SRI) or Transmission Loss (TL) is the dB reduction through the wall. To maximise the dB reduction we must use a wall with a lot of mass (kg) or, seen from the viewpoint of an approaching sound wave, one with a lot of kg behind every square metre, i.e. the kg m^{-2}. SRI increases in theory as 20 log M where M (in kg m^{-2}) is called the surface mass. Doubling the kg m^{-2} should thus increase the SRI by 6 dB, which is fine if you are starting with something light and do not mind a non-portable solution. In practice one only gains about 5 dB on doubling M.

The reader should interject that we are discussing insulation in terms of dB, whereas it is the dB (A) reduction that we need to tell us how effective the wall is in reducing hearing hazard. The problem is that the insulation provided varies markedly with frequency. Table 8.2 gives some values for materials of interest. These are approximate since the values obtained depend on the way in which they are measured and how the materials are mounted. For each material there is a gradual increase of SRI with frequency, in theory amounting to 6 dB for every frequency doubling but in practice of about 5 dB. This is shown in the central part of Figure 8.7. The poorer insulation at lower frequencies is familiar to anyone troubled by a neighbour's music; the bass notes come through the wall, leaving the treble parts behind. This behaviour is a nuisance to those seeking to reduce the intense low frequency sound from engine run-ups.

Since the insulation provided depends on the frequency content of the incoming sound we really need to calculate the reduction in each octave band in turn. Adding these contributions gives the overall sound level, in dB or dB (A) as in Chapter 3, and hence a single figure value for the insulation given by this particular wall material for this particular source. (This calculation is identical to that needed for evaluating hearing protection and is done in Chapter 9.) These calculations are lengthy and it is tempting to use published values of 'overall' insulation, often arithmetically averaged over a frequency range of 100 – 3150 Hz. Typical values are given in Table 8.3. The risk is that these may over-estimate the reduction at 250 Hz or so by more than 10 dB. Whether this matters, or not, depends on the low frequency content of the noise.

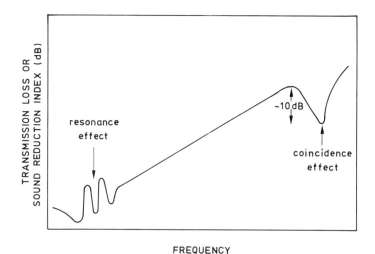

FREQUENCY

FIG. 8.7   Sound insulation and frequency

TABLE 8.2 SOUND REDUCTION INDICES

	kg m^{-2}	125Hz	250Hz	500Hz	1kHz	2kHz	4kHz
Walls							
19 mm chipboard sheets on wood frame	11	17	18	25	30	26	32
Hollow cinder concrete blocks, unpainted	75	27	32	37	40	41	45
Single 112.5 mm brick, plaster both sides	270	34	36	41	51	58	62
Single 225 mm brick, plaster both sides	480	41	45	48	56	65	69
Brick, 56 mm cavity, 12 mm plaster on							
outer faces	490	34	34	40	56	73	76
Windows							
Single glass in heavy frame 4 mm	11	21	23	27	33	34	26
6 mm	17	23	25	29	34	26	29
Double glazing*							
4 mm panes, 7 mm cavity	22	22	16	20	29	31	27
6 mm panes, 50 mm cavity	34	25	29	34	41	45	53
6 mm panes, 188 mm cavity	34	30	35	41	48	50	56
6 and 9 mm panes, 200mm cavity	42	36	45	58	59	55	66
(* panes in separate frames)							
Doors							
Panel, hollow core, normal hanging	9	12	13	14	16	18	24
Solid hardwood, normal hanging	28	17	21	26	29	31	34
Acoustic door, single sealed	70	20	28	36	41	45	43

TABLE 8.3 OVERALL SOUND INSULATION (AVERAGE OVER 100–3150 Hz)

	kg m^{-2}	Insulation
Single leaf		
203 mm hollow concrete block, plastered	244	45
112.5 mm brick, bare	220	35-40
112.5 mm brick, plastered	270	45
225 mm brick, plastered	480	50
254 mm concrete, plastered	635	52
Double leaf		
50 mm clinker block, 150 mm cavity, plastered both sides	185	47
112.5 mm brick, 50 mm cavity, plastered both sides	490	50-53
225 mm brick, 50 mm cavity, plastered both sides	930	55

A careful look at Table 8.2 shows some odd values in the single glass pane data; there is a minimum in the sound reduction obtained at 4 kHz for the 4 mm thickness and the minimum goes to lower frequencies as the surface mass increases for a thicker pane. What is happening is that the pane has bending waves travelling up it in response to the sound coming in at a particular angle; these bending waves are magnified if their peaks travel up the pane in company with peaks in the incoming sound. This is called the 'coincidence effect' since it requires the coincidence of the two waves involved. The same thing happens in a brick wall but the much greater surface mass involved sends the critical frequency down to 100 Hz or so. The effect is shown on Figure 8.7.

Figure 8.7 also shows strange wiggles at lowest frequencies. These are due to resonance in the panel, which makes an enhanced response to the incoming sound due to the waves travelling back and forth in the wall adding constructively.

This resonance effect crops up again with two-leaf walls and double glazing. The air linking the two components acts as a spring connecting them; when the air-gap is a half-wavelength then the spring goes into resonance and energy is transmitted easily from pane to pane. Otherwise the idea of a double partition is a good one as there are an extra two air–solid interfaces to reflect the sound back whence it came, rather than to allow it to pass on. The problem of achieving good insulation without using a single heavy wall is solved by using two lighter ones. The gap between the leaves should be greater than a half-wavelength for the lowest significant frequency present. An insulating blanket suspended in the cavity can help. The usual thermal double-glazing has too small a gap for efficient sound insulation.

Flanking Transmission

Table 8.2 includes some impressive figures for the insulation provided by barriers such as walls. These figures are, however, obtained in laboratories under conditions which may be unrealistic. For instance, actual walls are punctured by windows and doors, and by holes to allow the passage of pipes or cables. Windows may be poorly sealed into the surrounding walls. These conditions are carefully avoided in the laboratory tests, but we have to examine their effect.

Any process by which sound travels from one side of a wall to the other without going through the wall material itself is termed flanking transmission. Such transmission through acoustically weak areas in the wall reduces the actual amount of insulation it provides. It is pointless improving the insulation of the wall itself if the flanking path transmits just as much, or more, energy. There is nothing to be gained, for instance, in making walls thicker if most of the sound goes through the windows. The relative magnitude of these two contributions depends on areas and materials involved.

Without going into mathematical detail, we can follow the process by which the energy incident on the wall is divided into the two contributions on the receiver side from direct and flanking transmission. The significance of area arises simply from the energy flowing per second being the intensity ($W\ m^{-2}$) multiplied by area. If the incident intensity on the source side is I_s, the energy incident on the wall is $I_s A_1$ for a wall of area A_1. The amount penetrating to the other side will be $I_s A_1$ multiplied by the fraction of this incident energy that is transmitted. Writing this fraction conventionally as τ, the energy passing through the wall is $\tau_1 I_s A_1$, again using the suffix 1 for the wall. Similarly for a window we would have $\tau_2 I_s A_2$ as the energy transmitted, using suffix 2 for the window. Adding these contributions together we find that the effective fraction of the incident energy that is actually transmitted (τ_{eff}) is given by:

$$\tau_{eff} = \frac{A_1 \tau_1 + A_2 \tau_2}{A_1 + A_2}$$

The value of τ_{eff} is determined by the values of A and τ. A window would usually have a small area A_2 compared with the wall (A_1). But the values of τ may differ much more.

To find the values of τ, we use the fact that the Sound Reduction Index is just a way of putting τ, an energy ratio, into decibel form via the relation:

$$\text{SRI} = 10 \log \frac{1}{\tau}$$

Taking antilogs, it turns out that if for the wall the overall SRI is 40 dB, then $\tau_1 = 10^{-4}$, while for the window the SRI might be only 20 dB and $\tau_2 = 10^{-2}$, a factor of 100 greater. Thus even though A_2 is less than A_1 (say 1/10 of it), the product $A_2 \tau_2$ may well be much greater than $A_1 \tau_1$ and the window becomes the dominant contributor to the sound on the receiver side.

The calculations needed can be approximated by the nomogram of Figure 8.8, which shows the loss of insulation resulting from areas of lower-insulation in high-insulation walls. As seen above, the variables involved are the respective areas and the differences in the insulations, i.e. of τ. The actual sound level produced on the receiver side will be partly determined by the total absorption present in the receiving room; if there is little absorption the sound level will be increased.

For instance, take a hole of area 1/1000 of a wall. The hole lets all the incident sound through so that it has $\tau = 1$ and an SRI of 10 log 1, or zero. The wall may have an overall SRI of 50 dB. Their insulation difference, given across the diagram for each of the curves, is 50 dB and the 50 dB curve joins the 1:1000 area ratio at a point corresponding to 20 dB on the horizontal scale. We have lost 20 dB of effective insulation. In fact at low frequencies, where the wavelength of sound is greater than the width of the hole, the loss can be even greater than the calculation suggests.

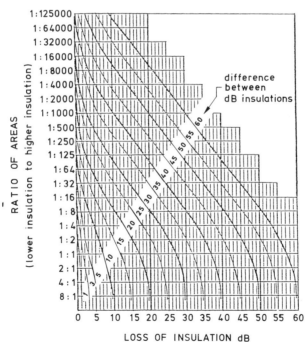

FIG. 8.8   Insulation loss in a composite wall

An office is to be moved close to an outdoor engine test facility where the dominant octave band level is 120 dB at 500 Hz. The adjoining wall is of brick of SRI 41 dB at 500 Hz and area 160 m², plus sealed windows of SRI 27 dB at 500 Hz and area 20 m². Estimate (a) the effective SRI of the wall and (b) the resulting octave band level in the office.

(a) The ratio of areas of low to high insulation is 1:8 and the difference in their SRIs is 14 dB, hence from Figure 8.8 the effective SRI is 41 − 6 = 35 dB at 500 Hz.

(b) Beware! *Very* approximately, it is 120 − 35 dB = 85 dB but SRI data apply to partitions between reverberant rooms and corrections have to be made when this condition is not met. Reverberant conditions certainly do not apply to the open-air side of a wall. Equations predicting received sound levels have been derived for common situations.

Example 1

Figure 8.9 shows the measured octave band levels at the operator's position close to a drone engine on test and in the adjacent control room. The insulation provided in each frequency band by the common wall, made of brick with a large well-sealed double-glazed observation window with 30 cm between the panes, is the appropriate vertical difference between two plots (in dB). The result is an overall reduction from 123 dB [120 dB(A)] to 90 dB [88 dB(A)], i.e. of 32 dB(A).

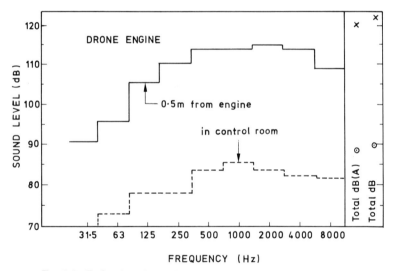

FIG. 8.9   Reduction of sound level in a control room (good design)

Example 2

Contrast this with Figure 8.10. Here a building has been adapted to house a series of engine test cells by installing lightweight partitions. The test cell is separated from the access corridor by a folding partition incorporating a large fan, and from the control area by a plasterboard wall containing an ill-fitting plywood door with a 2.5 cm gap along its base and two large double-glazed observation windows made up of flexible transparent plastic sheets 3 − 4 cm apart screwed to a wooden frame. There are small gaps around cables passing through this wall and two holes, of 3 and 4 cm diameter, into the test cell. The door between the control area and the corridor is wedged open during hot weather to provide air conditioning. The measured noise levels were as follows: in the engine test area, at full power, 112 dB(A), in the control room, at full power, 93 dB(A), giving an effective reduction of only 19 dB(A). Confirming one weakness in the partition, the sound level in the control area by the crack beneath the door was 104 dB(A).

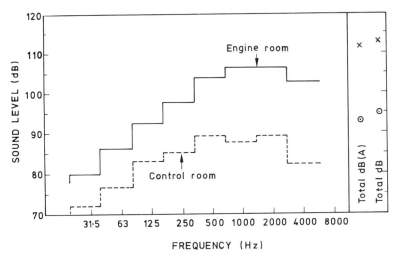

FIG. 8.10   Reduction of sound in a control room (poor design)

Example 3

One of the start-up compressors for the drone engines is also run in an adjacent open workshop used for their maintenance. The compressor is close to doors leading to adjacent offices and to an electronic repair vehicle. Two metres from the compressor the sound level is 94 dB(A) and it only drops below 90 dB(A) at a distance of 7 m. This variation with distance was not as uniform as in the lower plot of Figure 8.3 because this source is larger and we are still in the complicated 'near' sound field, and because a dominant frequency produced interference effects. Outside the repair vehicle door the level is 83 dB(A), and inside it 77 dB(A). It is not normal procedure for men in the workshop close to the power unit to wear hearing protection and unprotected personnel move to and fro into the adjacent offices, past the unit. With a running schedule of perhaps 4 hours, three times per week, the hazard due to this source alone for an individual moving normally around the area is small. The annoyance it creates could, however, be large. It is badly sited and it would be a relatively simple task to erect a lightweight insulating structure around it which was capable of reducing the highest radiated sound levels, between 500 and 2000 Hz.

Example 4

A small generator was required for use in a system which had to be inaudible to enemy patrols (see Chapter 11). Improving the exhaust and intake silencers is, by itself, insufficient since some of the noise is radiated from the body of the generator.

The requirement for a light weight portable enclosure dictated the use of double walls, since a single wall with the required attenuation would be too heavy. Figure 8.11 shows the enclosure. The air cooling ducts are lined with absorber and have several right-angled bends, to reduce sound transmission to the outside world.

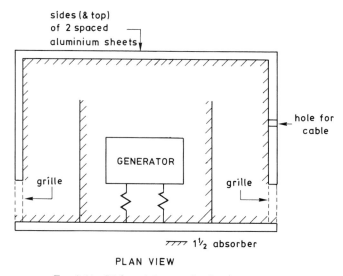

PLAN VIEW

FIG. 8.11   Lightweight sound reducing enclosure

Structure Borne Vibration

The previous discussion has concentrated on airborne sound. However, there is another way in which sound can be transmitted to an enclosure by machinery outside it. Vibration from the machinery can be transmitted through solid structures, such as girders and floor joists, and then be radiated as sound, expecially if the structure is rigidly attached to a large surface which can act as a sounding board.

The noise levels produced in this way are difficult to predict but can be very high. The problem is especially acute in large metal structures, such as tanks or ships. Tracked vehicles have a major problem in the vibration from track links hitting the ground, or passing over sprockets, which is transmitted through the vehicle structure. A study on the United States personnel carrier M113 showed that a substantial reduction in noise could be achieved by incorporating a flexible element into the track idler sprocket.

Structure borne vibration may be avoided by the use of flexible mountings (as used with the generator in Figure 8.11) which do not transmit vibration at frequencies above a few hertz. Ducting, pipes and cables will also need to be flexible. The use of such mountings will allow the vibration source to move slightly, and clearance must be allowed for this.

Recommended Sound Levels

It is only too common to see facilities such as electronic repair units, offices, crew rest areas and briefing rooms, where concentration and, possibly, telephone conversation is required, in close proximity to noisy sources. This is often the result of *ad hoc* changes of space usage or the movement of noisy sources, made with no regard for the noise problem. The noise implications of any such changes should include any likely effects on the working efficiency of personnel as well as of possible hazard.

This raises the question of the recommended sound levels for the various working areas. One system, entitled Noise Rating, gave octave band curves that should not be exceeded for various environments. The Noise Rating was approximately the dB(A) level minus 5 or 10. This gave the following recommended maximum levels: workshop 70–75 dB(A), general office, 60–65 dB(A). An RAF proposal shown in Table 8.3, from a Defence Standard source document, reduces these levels, specifies both the maximum acceptable L_{eq} and the maximum dB(A) levels, and defines working areas more carefully. Similar naval requirements (STANAG 1186) are given in Table 8.4, which indicates the difficulty of providing quiet areas on board ship. This is particularly due to transmission around the solid structure of the hull.

TABLE 8.3 RECOMMENDED ENVIRONMENT SOUND LEVELS (RAF)

Category	Environmental area/buildings	Maximum acceptable L_{eq} dB(A)	Maximum SPL dB(A)
Group B	Where health, efficiency and/or safety could be affected by noise and where the use of personal protective equipment is impracticable	80	100
Group C	Communication areas:		
	(1) Minimal communication, i.e. danger signals; restricted, pre-arranged vocabulary	80	100
	(2) Intermittent communication, i.e. heavy machinery workshops and similar situations	70	90
	(3) Continuous communications in work areas, i.e. electronic workshop stores areas, general offices, etc.	55	80
	(4) Operational communication area of electronically aided communcation where aircraft safety might be involved	40	70
	(5) Lecturing, briefing or debriefing	40	70
	(6) Private offices (not more than two occupants)	45	75
Group D	(1) Quiet leisure areas, i.e. off-duty pursuits that involve mental effort and concentration	45	75
	(2) Public leisure areas, Messes and the like	55	74
Group E	Rest, sleeping and clinical areas	35	75

TABLE 8.4 Recommended Environment Sound Levels (STANAG 1186)

Grade	Criteria	Environmental area/buildings	Maximum SPL dB(A)
A	A high degree of concentration or listening is required	Electronic Warfare Office Sick Bays	60
B	Easy speech communication is necessary or sleep is not disturbed	Cabins and Messdecks Sonar Control Room Wireless and Signal Office Enclosed Bridge Operations Room	65
C	Good speech communication and personnel comfort are required	Dining Halls Offices Main Passageways Separate Machinery Control Room Recreation Spaces on Deck	70
D	Voice communication is necessary but a raised level is acceptable	Bathrooms Galleys Stores Workshops Remainder of Upper Deck	80
E	Unassisted voice communication is not required and the use hearing protection (if required) is acceptable	Any space where the noise generated within the compartment is regularly above 80 dB(A) e.g. certain machinery spaces and workshops	90

Noise Control at Source

A detailed discussion of methods of noise control is beyond the scope of this book, but the following notes give some possible approaches. For more detail see the Bibliography. While substantial reductions in noise emission may often be difficult and costly to achieve, comparatively minor modification can often give worthwhile reductions.

In general, noise control is most effective and cheapest when the mechanisms of noise production are identified and corrected at an early stage in the design and installation of equipment. The United Kingdom Health and Safety Executive document '100 Practical Applications of Noise Reduction Methods' (HSE, 1983) shows some of the possible approaches.

The first stage is to measure or estimate the noise. The use of narrow-band frequency analysis can often be used to identify a specific frequency associated with one component from a noisy equipment, for instance an engine firing frequency or, in the case of tracked vehicles, a track-link passage frequency.

Where off-the-shelf equipment is installed, its noise emission should be known so that its addition to the noise in a workshop or enclosure can be estimated. Noise specifications should be included in all requirement specifications. However, the noise level will also depend on the size of the enclosed space in which the equipment is installed, on the nature of its internal surfaces and on any barriers between the equipment and the workforce.

Other stages include:—

Vibration isolation — Vibrating parts can be isolated from large surfaces, and from floors and other structures which could transmit or radiate vibration. Vibration isolators, made from a variety of materials, are widely available. Pipework and ducting should incorporate flexible connectors.

Use of alternative work processes — e.g. pressure sealing instead of riveting, screwing rather than hammering, and using lower flow velocities in air or gas systems.

Improved maintenance — to remedy steam leaks, badly worn bearings or gears, poor lubrication, loose parts, slapping belts or unbalanced rotating parts.

Modification of noise sources — gears can be redesigned or made from plastic materials. Moving parts can be reduced, made to move more slowly or balanced. Sheet metal guards can be replaced by wire mesh.

Use of mufflers and silencers — not only on petrol and diesel engines, but also on exhausts or discharges of steam, compressed air and other gases. Silencers can also be fitted into air ducts.

Summary

This chapter has been concerned with the problem of how to reduce internal noise levels. The solutions have required an understanding of how sound propagates in enclosed spaces because this determines the strategy to be used in attempting to reduce the noise level. Both the absorbers and insulators vary in their behaviour with frequency. Good insulation particularly requires great care in removing gaps through which sound can easily penetrate. In the last resort, hearing protection will be required if sound levels cannot be reduced enough (Chapter 9). Levels low enough not to provide a hazard may still affect performance or produce annoyance (Chapter 10).

Figure 8.12 illustrates many of the points discussed in this chapter. The grinding wheel is an increasingly common workshop tool and in this case the large pipe will act as a sounding board. The rigid wall behind will act as a good reflector of sound; it is hoped that there is no office behind the door. Two forms of hearing protection described in the next chapter are being worn, the foam plug and the ear muff. Note that the sound level meter is being held well away from the body and the windshield is being used to protect the microphone from small fragments.

FIG. 8.12   A typical workshop problem

SELF TEST QUESTIONS

Question 1   Explain the inverse square law of intensity against distance from a source. If it holds, show that the sound level reduction should be 6 dB on doubling the distance.

Answer ....

....

....

Question 2   What is meant by:
(a)   Absorption coefficient of a surface,
(b)   Total absorption of a room?
Assuming that the sound intensity at a point in a room is inversely proportional to the total absorption present, show that doubling the absorption would reduce the sound level by 3 dB.

Answer ....

....

....

Question 3   A wall without doors has an overall SRI of 55 dB. What is the effect on this of adding a door of SRI = 22 dB filling 1/20 of the wall area when (a) the door is shut and (b) open?

Answer ....

....

....

Question 4   The table show octave band data (in dB) obtained for a Harrier on a pre-flight check as measured in a room 20 m away, with a flimsy door facing onto the apron, open and shut. Estimate the respective dB and dB(A) levels and comment.

Centre Frequency (Hz)	31.5	63	125	250	500	1000	2000	4000	8000
Door open (dB)	98	101	97	97.5	98	103	101	105	102
Door shut (dB)	92.5	94	92.5	92	91.5	97	93	94	92

Answer ....

....

....

Answers on page 115.

9. Hearing Protection

Hearing protectors, such as ear muffs, ear plugs and noise-excluding helmets, are very widely used in both military and civil practice to reduce noise reaching the ear. This chapter shows how the effectiveness of these protectors can be estimated, the circumstances in which their use is appropriate, the disadvantages which may stem from their use, the compromises which may have to be made and the practical factors which limit their effectiveness. While the potential benefits of hearing protectors are very substantial, they should never be used as a substitute for other methods of noise reduction.

Education in the use of hearing protection is vital for hearing conservation. Some questions that illustrate important points are raised and answered in this chapter.

Hearing Protectors

A hearing protector is simply an item of personal equipment which reduces the noise reaching the ear. In this respect it is much like an acoustical barrier or enclosure, except that it is worn by the individual rather than applied to the noise source. Hearing protectors are relatively inexpensive and can be very effective, and hence they are widely used.

Hearing protectors are of three main types:

▶ Ear plugs, which fit into the outer part of the ear canal.
▶ Ear muffs, which fit on to the side of the head and enclose the ear.
▶ Noise-excluding helmets as used in aircraft or tanks. These have inbuilt ear muffs, which provide most of the protection. The helmet outer shell by itself provides relatively little.

Ear Plugs

Ear plugs are usually of two types:

▶ Prefabricated plugs made from a rubbery plastic material, moulded in a shape intended to fit into the ear canal. Usually one or more flanges are provided to ensure a good seal against the sides of the canal. Several sizes must be provided, since the size of the ear canal varies considerably between different individuals. It is also possible for the two ear canals of one man to be of different sizes.
▶ A malleable material which is shaped by the user to fit his own ears. Various types of material have been used, including Glass Down (which is a very fine non-irritant form of glass fibre, usually with a thin plastic sheath), and

an expanded foam resin material. In practice, such ear plugs need to be replaced at intervals and are often regarded as disposable throw-away items to be replaced on each occasion of noise exposure.

It is also possible to make ear plugs permanently moulded to fit the individual ear. In practice, they are not outstandingly successful, and for military use are unlikely to repay the effort required to produce them.

The fit of the ear plug into the ear canal is of vital importance; if an effective seal is not made, the ear plug will not protect. It requires a definite effort on the part of the user. Merely stuffing them into the canal in the hope that they won't fall out is not good enough! This also requires that the correct size of prefabricated ear plug is chosen. It sounds easy enough, but in both military and civil practice the wrong size is often used, again leading to very poor protection.

Ear Muffs

Ear muffs do not suffer from a fitting problem; the ear cup can be made to accommodate any size ear, and the headband is usually adjustable. Their main problem is that they clash with other items of headgear, especially helmets, whether they are military combat helmets or industrial safety helmets. This clash is not inevitable, but depends on the design of both the ear muff and the helmet. Their effectiveness is also reduced by anything which interrupts the seal between the ear and the side of the head. Spectacle or safety goggle frames, the NBC fabric hood and respirator, long hair, beards, etc., will all do this (Figure 6.4 shows an example). The worst offender is the Army beret, neatly pulled over to one side of the head so that a fold of material gets under the ear muff seal.

Ear muffs are also more fragile than other protectors; they are readily broken by careless use. The seals on the ear cups are affected by sweat and body oils, and they harden with use; they then need replacing. They will also break if handled in Arctic conditions. Fluid-filled seals are especially vulnerable. Once the fluid leaks out, the muffs are useless until the seals are replaced.

Noise-excluding helmets provide a neat all-in-one solution. Of course different designs tend to be needed for different jobs, and they are expensive. Their effectiveness is reduced by anything between the ear cup and the side of the head, as with ear muffs.

Hearing protectors are often found to be uncomfortable, especially when worn for prolonged periods in hot conditions. There does seem to be a genuine difference between individuals, as some men have more of a problem than others; there may be a personal preference for ear muffs rather than ear plugs, or vice versa. Their acceptability depends on the design of the protectors; in the case of ear muffs, for instance, an excessive or uneven pressure on the side of the head will cause discomfort. Prefabricated ear plugs are found by some users to be especially uncomfortable.

Comparison of Protectors

The advantages of the different types of protection are summarised in Table 9.1.

TABLE 9.1 COMPARISON OF EAR PROTECTORS

Type	Advantages	Disadvantages
Prefabricated ear plugs (moulded, re-usable)	Cheap	Serious sizing problem Can cause excessive discomfort
Ear plugs (malleable, moulded by user)	Cheap at first	Cost mounts up as plugs need to be replaced
Ear muffs	Relatively popular with users No fitting problems	Fragile Clash with other headgear Effectiveness lost if seal interrupted
Noise-excluding helmets	All-in-one solution	Expensive Effectiveness lost if seal interrupted

This list is not exhaustive, and the reader can probably add to it. For instance, in Arctic conditions, can you get ear plugs out of a container and into your ears while wearing mitts?

Does it really matter if the protector is uncomfortable? The man will wear it if he's ordered to.

Obviously you are doing a staff job. Try looking on a range, or in a workshop. You will find that no-one uses protective equipment unless he wants to! If the device isn't comfortable — or, for that matter, it is not available, or the user is not convinced that it is necessary — it will not be used.

In an emergency, will fingers-in-the-ear do?

Provided the ear canal is effectively closed, this will protect the ear quite well, but you need to have both hands free! As soon as you remove your hand to do a job, the protection is lost. One operator near the power unit shown in Figure 8.10 used fingers instead of protectors. He removed a hand to find and use a handkerchief, leaving that ear exposed to 112 dB(A) for about 1 min — the allowed daily dose of that level is under 3 minutes on the $L_{eq(8)} = 90$ dB(A) standard and less than 1 min on the 85 dB(A) standard. Cupping the ear in the hand is of little use due to the gaps around the hand.

This is all very well, but the job of a hearing protector is to protect. How well does it keep the noise out? All these practical factors are of secondary importance.

No. Practical factors are of primary importance. To state the obvious; if the device is to protect, it must be used correctly. Unfortunately, we have to admit from practical observation and experience that hearing protection is often not used at all, or is used incorrectly, even during intense noise exposure. 'The best hearing protector is the one that is worn.'

There is not much benefit from a protector which gives marvellous results in a laboratory test, if it's left on the shelf! Most of the cases of noise-induced hearing loss seen in Army practice results from failure to use any protection at all. However, we will go on to see how the protection can be measured. We will find that it is relatively easy to measure this in the laboratory; but how well does the laboratory correspond to real life?

Attenuation of Noise by Hearing Protectors

The difference in the noise reaching the ear with and without the protector is termed the attenuation. It depends on the frequency of the noise. It also varies between different users, so it is necessary to make measurements on a number of individuals, and then find the mean and standard deviation of the attenuation at each frequency. Figure 9.1 shows typical results for an ear muff.

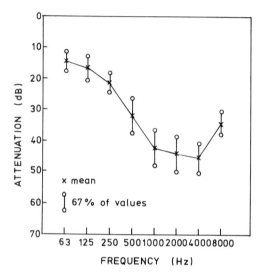

FIG. 9.1   Attenuation by an ear-muff

The method used in current standards is to find the difference in hearing thresholds with and without the protector in place. This, of course, requires use of a very quiet room in which to do the tests; because suitable rooms are few in number and very expensive to construct, only highly specialised acoustic laboratories can perform the test. Perhaps surprisingly, results from this test relate very well to tests performed in much more intense noise.

Tests performed according to British and International standards (BS 5108, ISO 4869) go to a great deal of trouble to find representative subjects, selected to have good hearing but otherwise taken at random from the general population. Unfortunately, this has not always been true in American practice. A minimum of 10 subjects is required but it is better to use more if possible. Subjects are required to remove spectacles and any other headgear which could affect the seal of an ear muff.

At one time it was usual to take the mean value of attenuation as an indication of the protection that the user received. A moment's thought will show that this is not fair to half the users, who will receive less than the mean attenuation — the other half will receive more. Figure 9.2 shows idealised results for a large number of measurements of the attenuation (in dB) obtained at one frequency. These are ideal in that they follow what is termed a normal distribution curve. In practice this is not important if we stay close to the mean value shown by the peak. The standard deviation shows how much the attenuation varies between different users. If the standard deviation is large it shows that some individual users are getting much more that others, which is unfortunate for the others! European practice has therefore been to subtract the standard deviation from the mean attenuation, to yield a quantity known as assumed protection. About 83% of users will get more protection than the value of the assumed protection, as shown in Figure 9.2. American practice has, in some cases, been to subtract twice the standard deviation.

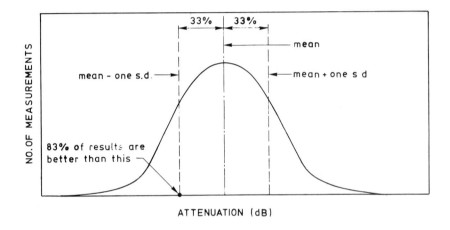

Fig. 9.2   Statistics of hearing protectors

The obvious problem with this procedure is that the subjects, having removed any spectacles, are sitting in a comfortable laboratory. They have studied the instructions provided by the manufacturer. Then they carefully put on a new and undamaged protector 'having made several up-and-down and right-to-left movements of the head while opening and closing the lower jaw after final fitting' as specified in BS 5108. How closely does this correspond to real life? A number of studies on hearing protection in civil and military use have shown that the protection in real life is less than laboratory test methods indicate. The difference depends on how carefully the protector is used, how carefully it is maintained, and what other headgear is used at the same time. All that can be said with certainty is that the test results give a value which can be approached under ideal conditions.

With that reservation in mind, we can look at values of attenuation, obtained from the laboratory test, for various types of protector.

The values in Table 9.2 are intended only as an illustration of what various types of protector are likely to achieve. In a real-life case, it will be necessary to obtain data on the specific model of protector being considered; the manufacturer will normally supply results from a standard test.

TABLE 9.2 ATTENUATION FROM VARIOUS TYPES OF PROTECTOR

Protector type		Frequency (Hz)									
		63	125	250	500	1000	2000	3150	4000	6300	8000
Glass Down	mean	4	6	8	11	15	19	26	26	33	35
ear plug	sd	3	4	5	5	4	5	5	5	6	5
V51R	mean	20	20	19	19	22	27	32	29	29	30
prefabricated ear plug	sd	6	7	7	7	6	5	5	6	12	10
E-A-R expanded	mean	25	26	27	29	30	33	43	44	45	44
foam ear plug	sd	7	8	7	7	6	5	5	5	5	6
Popular	mean	10	8	14	23	31	32	40	36	31	31
industrial ear muff	sd	5	4	4	6	6	5	5	5	7	6
High quality	mean	17	19	24	32	41	38	43	42	29	32
eaf muff (liquid-filled seal)	sd	6	5	4	4	5	5	4	6	5	6
Flying helmet	mean	16	12	13	27	34	33	39	44	49	52
	sd	4	4	5	3	4	4	5	6	7	6
High-attenuation	mean	17	18	22	28	25	26	38	37	35	33
communications headset	sd	7	6	5	5	7	5	7	7	5	5
Same headset,	mean	26	30	35	36	38	39	48	50	46	45
used with E-A-R expanded foam ear plug	sd	8	6	5	7	5	5	6	6	4	5

There are several other points to note about this table.

First, test results are often given to the nearest 0.1 dB. This is quite pointless, since their accuracy does not really justify it; in Table 9.2 all values have been rounded to the nearest dB.

Secondly, the test results usually include results for 3150 and 6300 Hz. This information cannot be used in the assessment of noise at the ear, which relies on the octave band levels of the noise; 3150 and 6300 Hz are not octave band centre frequencies. Sometimes the test results also omit 63 Hz, which is a difficult frequency at which to measure accurately. Measurements are rarely made at 31.5 Hz or at 16,000 Hz, since the 'A' weighted octave band levels at these frequencies are usually not very high.

Thirdly, it is quite obvious that all the hearing protectors give better results at mid and high frequencies than at low frequencies. This is more marked with ear muffs than with ear plugs. Protection against noise is especially difficult where the noise contains strong low-frequency components.

Finally, the use of ear plugs at the same time as an ear muff or headset gives only a slight improvement compared with the use of either by itself. Use of double hearing protection is only indicated for exceptionally noisy situations. Even then, only highly motivated specialist personnel are likely to use it effectively.

Quite obviously, some of the protectors give better protection than others. Look at the 'popular industrial ear muff', for instance. It is not nearly so good as the high-quality ear muff with the liquid filled seal. Surely we should supply only the best hearing protection, the protectors which give the most attentuation?

If the environment is very noisy, this is true. However, it often happens that, if the noise is only slightly above damaging levels, the use of hearing protection brings the noise at the ear well below damaging levels, even with the protectors with the more modest attenuation. In that case, there simply isn't any point in reducing it further. The high-attenuation ear muffs have definite disadvantages, too. Apart from being fairly expensive, they tend to be bulky, less compatible with helmets and other headgear, less comfortable and perhaps more fragile. In other words, there is more to the choice of a hearing protector than picking the one with the most attenuation.

How do I work out the effectiveness of a particular protector in my job?

▶ Measure the octave band sound pressure levels of the noise.

▶ Subtract the standard deviation from the mean attenuation to give the assumed protection in each octave band.

▶ Subtract the assumed protection from the octave band sound pressure level in each octave band.

▶ Apply an 'A' weighting.

▶ Add the band levels to find the 'A' weighted sound pressure level at the ear. Compare this with the maximum permissible 'A' weighted sound pressure level for the required exposure duration.

It is tedious but straightforward. A worked example follows.

Calculation of effective attenuation

The octave band spectrum inside a tracked vehicle running at 50 km/h was measured as:

Frequency Hz	63	125	250	500	1000	2000	4000	8000
Level dB	110	124	120	111	106	94	83	93

The protector chosen was an ear muff with the following attenuation, in dB:

Mean	16	12	16	25	35	36	37	32
sd	4	4	3	4	4	4	2	5

so that each assumed protection of mean — 1 sd was:

dB	12	8	13	21	31	32	35	27

Subtracting the assumed protections from the octave band levels gives the octave band levels at the ear:

dB	98	116	107	90	75	62	48	66

Reduce to 'A' weighted levels by adding the corrections:

dB	−26	−16	−9	−3	0	1	1	−1

giving 'A' weighted levels in each octave band:

dB(A)	72	100	98	87	75	63	49	65

Using the method of Chapter 3, this adds up to 102 dB(A)

The original noise levels before hearing protection, converted to dB(A), are:

dB(A)	84	108	111	108	106	95	84	92

which adds up to 115 dB(A).

The muff is reducing the noise reaching the ear from 115 to 102 dB(A). This assumes the attenuation data were correct and that the usage of the muff in the vehicle bears at least some relation to the way it was used in the laboratory! If a noise exposure of 90 dB(A) for 8 h is considered tolerable, then the maximum exposure duration is 30 min with protection, against 90 s without it. If the maximum noise exposure is 85 dB(A) over 8 h, the corresponding durations are 10 min and 30 s respectively.

The dominance of low frequencies is typical of noise inside vehicles and in many other situations; the effect of the ear muff in this case is almost entirely determined by its attenuation at 125 and 250 Hz. In principle, the use of the ear muff with a better low-frequency attenuation would have reduced the noise at the ear quite substantially, but such an ear muff would probably not have met the requirement for compatibility with a combat helmet, as this particular muff does.

Is there an easier way of doing this calculation?

Single figure indices of attenuation, to be subtracted from the noise level measured in dB(A), have been proposed. This only works if it is assumed that the noise has a 'typical' spectrum. This is hard to justify even in an industrial context. In a military context there is too much variation in possible spectra for the method to be helpful.

It may be possible to get an approximate answer for levels at the ear in dB(A), starting from levels in dB(C); an International Standard along these lines is still being considered. However, the calculation given above will still be needed if an accurate answer is required.

What about gunfire noise?

The method shown above is not really practical for gunfire noise. The usual solution is to make an allowance which is generally specified in standards for maximum impulse noise exposure. As a guide, the use of protection gives, effectively, a reduction in peak level of about 20 dB, or even more for some specific types of protector. The expanded foam (E-A-R) ear plug has been shown to be particularly good, provided it is fitted correctly.

What happens to the protection from an ear muff or helmet if an NBC jacket hood, and/or respirator, is used at the same time?

The porous fabric of the hood introduces a leakage path beneath the ear muff seal; the straps of the respirator have the same effect. The attenuation at low frequencies can easily be reduced to zero, and at higher frequencies will still be much less (by as much as 20 dB) than without the hood or respirator.

The following results for a tank crewman's helmet, worn without and with an NBC jacket hood, show this clearly (Table 9.3). Note, incidentally, the rather poor attenuation even without the hood, indicating a poor fit with this helmet. (Fortunately, after many years in service, the helmet is now being replaced!)

TABLE 9.3 EFFECT OF NBC HOOD ON HELMET ATTENUATION

		63	125	250	500	Frequency (Hz) 1000	2000	3150	4000	6300	8000
Without hood	mean	5	3	11	23	26	26	29	29	17	17
	sd	5	3	3	2	7	9	7	7	8	7
With hood	mean	0	−2	2	11	14	12	14	19	14	16
	sd	1	2	2	4	7	4	4	4	5	6

With the hood, the fit is so bad with this helmet that the attenuation at 125 Hz is negative, due probably to a resonance in the air under the ear cups and the gap between the seal and the side of the head.

Incidentally, the attenuation given by the NBC hood alone, and by other fabric hoods such as parka hoods, is very small.

Surely it will not make much more difference if I take the protector off for a few minutes?

It will make quite a lot of difference! Look at the example given a little earlier, with the use of an ear muff in an armoured vehicle. Here, removing the protector for 90 s means that you should have no more noise exposure at all on the same day.

As a general rule, it is much better to provide a moderately effective protector which is always worn, than a very effective one which is worn only most of the time.

Table 9.4 shows the effective protection offered by a muff worn only part of the time. Assume that the 'A' weighted sound pressure level at the ear is reduced by 30 dB(A) when the ear muff is worn; this implies a fairly good ear muff and a mainly high-frequency noise. Total duration of the noise exposure is 8 h.

TABLE 9.4 EFFECT OF THE TIME WORN ON MUFF PROTECTION

Time worn	Effective muff protection
8 h	30 dB(A)
7 h 55 min	20
7 h 12 min	10
4 h	3

Quite a lot of the men I work with say that they can't hear speech or other sounds when they wear hearing protectors. I don't seem to have this trouble. Is it just an excuse not to wear them?

Well, it could be, but their problem could be genuine. For someone with normal hearing, the use of hearing protectors reduces both speech and noise in the same proportion, so the ability to understand speech is not affected. However, if they have a high-frequency hearing loss, perhaps as a result of noise exposure, the effect of this combined with the high-frequency attenuation of the protector could easily mean that they cannot hear the high-frequency components of speech at all.

Other factors could be important. For instance, it is natural to speak more loudly in a noisy place. If you wear hearing protection, it will not seem so noisy, so you will not speak so loudly and consequently it will be more difficult for someone to hear you. It can also be more difficult to hear where a sound comes from if you are wearing hearing protection. Urgent warning sounds may not be perceived as urgent if they do not sound loud. The problem is made worse if the type of protection chosen provides more attenuation than is necessary.

Intense noise occurring periodically on a quiet background is a special case. Gunfire noise on an otherwise quiet range is an obvious example. It is possible to make hearing protectors which have a greater attenuation for intense sound than for lower levels such as speech. Of the many amplitude sensitive protectors that have been designed, one which can actually work is an ear plug which depends on the change from laminar to turbulent airflow through a small orifice. Another is an ear muff with an external microphone, a peak-limiting amplifier and an internal telephone transducer. It is advisable, before procuring these items, to secure independent assessment of their effectiveness.

If there are standards for measuring attenuation, are there also standards for measuring other qualities, such as comfort or robustness?

Yes; the British Standard 6344, for instance, does this. In the case of ear muffs, it specifies durability, comfort in terms of maximum headband force and the maximum pressure exerted by the seal on the side of the head, flammability, etc. Although it is intended for industrial use, many of the tests have a wider application. Procurement of hearing protectors should always require observance of this or a similar standard. An International Standard on similar lines is in preparation.

So what is the best form of hearing protection for military use?

It should be obvious by now that there is not a single type that is best for all circumstances. Also, individuals vary, and if a wide choice is provided, then an individual is more likely to find a type that suits him.

Leaving aside protectors with a special function, such as communications sets, helmets, and amplitude-sensitive protectors, there is a need for three basic types of protector:

▶ An ear plug is needed since much military headgear is not compatible with ear muffs. Also, ear plugs are easily carried and unbreakable, major virtues on military exercises. The sizing problem with prefabricated ear plugs has proved intractable, so that leaves the disposable ear plug. The foam resin variety has proved particularly successful although other types could be used.

▶ Ear muffs are strongly preferred by the user where practical; this includes many range jobs as well as workshops and vehicles. The requirement is for a robust ear muff which is compatible, as far as possible, with other military equipment, including helmets.

▶ For the relatively few situations where the above ear muff does not provide sufficient protection, a high-attenuation ear muff is required. In order to obtain the extra attenuation, compatibility with other equipment and robustness may have to be sacrificed.

Conclusions

The effectiveness of a hearing protector can be calculated, given measurements of the noise in octave bands. The calculation will only be valid if the protector is correctly used on all occasions of exposure.

Factors such as robustness, comfort and compatibility with other equipment are just as important as acoustical effectiveness — the device will not work unless the user is able and willing to wear it! Although the attenuation is important, it is a mistake to consider only this aspect.

Self Test Questions

Question 1   Repeat the calculation for a tracked vehicle with an E-A-R expanded foam plug to find the effective dB(A) reduction provided. Use plug attenuation data from Table 9.2. What is the allowed exposure duration on the 90 dB(A)–8 h criterion?

Answer   ....

....

....

Question 2   A VC-10 aircraft on a detuner gave the following octave band levels at a ground crew position:

Frequency	63	125	250	500	1000	2000	4000	8000
dB	107	112	114	119	123	121	116	105

Calculate the dB(A) reduction provided by the muff used in the text calculation under 'Calculation of Effective Attenuation'.

Answer   ....

....

....

Answers on page 116.

10. Noise, Performance, Annoyance and Health

The Problem
Sound at levels high enough to cause a hazard to hearing is also undesirable if it creates other health problems, interferes with performance of a task or produces annoyance. Sound below hazardous levels may still affect performance or annoy, and hence would still be regarded as noise. Many military tasks such as target tracking or setting up complex equipment require concentration to be sustained over long periods. Noise may have a direct effect on the performance of the task or an indirect one via the irritation or mental fatigue it produces. Off-duty personnel requiring adequate rest close to noisy areas need some consideration.

Noise and Performance
It must be said at the outset that this remains a very contentious area. There are great difficulties in predicting the effect on an individual due to the very large variation in human response. A familiar example of variable response is: a technician appears with a sound level meter. Does morale, and hence performance, increase, as the management are at last doing something about the noise problem, or decrease, as there is obviously a problem here that we didn't know about?

It is also surprisingly difficult to set up experiments that can precisely answer the questions that arise. The strictly-controlled conditions under which laboratory investigations are made can be poles apart from the conditions inside a noisy, vibrating and hot vehicle. The interpretation of the results of experiments is often uncertain and many results say more about the experimental technique used than about the subjects.

Sources of Stress
Noise is only one source of stress, or stressor, in many such situations and it can be difficult to separate the effect of the various stressors.

Example:

A military communications room 5 m long by 3 m wide housed 12 punched-tape machines and operators working 12 h shifts. It had no windows and inadequate air-conditioning. Complaints made concerned the noise level, the difficulty of verbal communication and general fatigue at the end of the shift. The machines punch out messages at random with typically three operating at once. The noise level at the centre of the room was 80 ± 1 dB(A). The spectrum from each machine peaked at 2000–4000 Hz, in the region of highest ear sensitivity and crucial for understanding speech. The machines were old and continually breaking down so that the noise-insulating hoods provided by the manufacturers were left open to allow frequent insertion of screwdrivers. During these adjustments, operators were exposed to 84 dB(A). There are many stressors at work here. Is noise reducing efficiency? How can its effects be separated from the other factors, such as frustration with the equipment, that made this an unpopular job?

Factors Affecting Performance

The effect of noise on the performance of a task depends on the nature of the noise, the nature of the task and the response of the individual involved.

The nature of the noise includes not only physically-measurable quantities such as intensity, loudness, frequency content, variation with time and duration, but also its ability to distract by being unfamiliar or unexpected. The nature of the task ranges from the simple, repetitive and boring to the complex, requiring sustained concentration and mental agility. The response of the individual could be to perform the task more slowly, to make more errors or to change his approach to the task. What does one take as a measure of performance?

There are basically two approaches to measuring the effect of the noise. One is a field trial in which the noise source is varied but all the other environmental effects remain constant; these have been rare. The other, more academic, approach is the laboratory test in which there is close control on the noise and the task in an attempt to see how specific sounds affect specific types of task; the problem then is often that the sounds and tasks are too unrealistic for the results to be applied to such problems as 'will the tank commander make incorrect decisions because the sound level is 100 dB(A) inside his helmet?' and 'will his driver still be alert after 2 h at a similar level?'

Overall, it has been very difficult to substantiate the common view that noise has an adverse effect on performance in general, although it will do for tasks involving verbal communication or auditory signals. Many experiments have been inconclusive or unreliable due to inadequate control of all the variables involved.

There is thus still no definitive statement about the way in which noise affects performance. A few overall conclusions have emerged however, that are relevant to military tasks:

▶ Continuous noise without special meaning, which would tend to distract, does little to impair performance below 90 dB(A).

▶ Impulsive and intermittent noises are more disruptive than continuous noise of the same level.

▶ High frequency noise components affect performance more than low frequencies.

▶ Noise tends to increase error rather than decrease the work rate.

▶ A greater loss of performance occurs with tasks requiring prolonged concentration or where more than one task is performed at the same time. Simple repetitive tasks are little affected or may even be improved in performance.

Arousal

A useful theory which explains some of the above conclusions are based on the idea of arousal. Arousal describes the level of our behavioural activity, ranging from sleep to the highly alert state. The reader's state of arousal will have varied widely while reading this book. Noise increases arousal when the state of arousal is low and this can improve performance on monotonous tasks. If the noise level is too high, however, arousal becomes too high and performance falls. The over-aroused man is in a hurry and is likely to make mistakes.

Noise and Annoyance

All levels of sound can create annoyance, from a dripping tap to a low flying jet. The annoyance may be the direct result of the sound or an indirect one due, for instance, to the need to close windows in hot weather.

We discussed in Chapter 4 the constant-loudness curves which are derived by subjects judging two sounds to be equally loud. This is a fairly reproducible experiment and different individuals will agree that one sound is as loud as the other. They may well not agree that the two sounds are equally annoying since there are subjective effects involving the actual nature of the sound. This is the difference between loudness and noisiness; music for one man is noise for another.

An individual's tolerance of noise includes many factors, including:

▶ Who is producing it.
▶ Whether it is his employer who is responsible, in other words if a job goes with the noise.
▶ Whether the producer is thought to be doing his best to reduce it (e.g. by restricting the number of flights, increasing flying height or restricting range firings).
▶ Whether the activity producing the noise is thought necessary (pilot training or joy-rides?).
▶ How good the noise producer is at public relations.
▶ The context in which the noise is heard.

Prediction of Annoyance

Predicting the likely response of an individual to a particular noise is almost impossible and all that can be done is to make social surveys of large groups of people, asking them to rank various noises in annoyance order. The outcome is various attempts to quantify likely annoyance in terms of the noise level, the number of occurrences and characteristics such as the presence of whines or bangs. It is not the intention here to describe in detail specialised procedures such as those for predicting aircraft noise nuisance, partly because L_{eq} seems to be as good a guide as any of the more complicated procedures and is used as such by the RAF, but only to indicate the generally relevant problems.

One attempt at predicting annoyance due to industrial noise (British Standard 4142) assumes that complaints will arise if the noise level outside the affected dwelling is 10 dB(A) or more above the background level. The noise level is corrected by adding 5 dB(A) if there is any tonal content detected as whines, or an impulsive content; a reduction is made if the noise is not continuous but intermittent.

There has been strong criticism of BS 4142 for not predicting complaints when many have arisen. In particular the tonal correction is thought to be inadequate and intermittent noise is more annoying, not less, than continuous noise. It also applies to the noise measured outside whereas the annoyance is often being created indoors. But the criticism that concerns us most here is that the dB(A) does not effectively rank annoyance due to low frequency sources. This point is worth elaboration due to the large number of such sources in the military environment.

Low Frequency Effects

There are several reasons for the annoyance problems that arise from low frequency sound:

▶ Low frequencies are more readily transmitted in air than the higher frequencies.

▶ The fact that long wavelengths are involved means that barriers and buildings are less effective in blocking the sound.

▶ Parts of building structures may resonate in response to low frequency sound.

Many floors and slabs have natural frequencies in the range of 10 – 100 Hz; window panes give values from 10 to 100 Hz, the lower frequencies corresponding to larger windows. Window vibration due to the passage of a Chinook can cause much greater annoyance than the dB(A) value would suggest. Vibration of the house structure, evidenced by rattling ornaments, often becomes associated with a fear, even if unfounded, of eventual structural damage.

Infrasound

Figure 4.2 showed how the threshold of audibility of the ear increased as the frequency dropped. Going beyond that graph, typical values are 100 dB at 10 Hz, 120 dB at 3Hz and 140 dB at 1Hz. Sound of frequency below 20 Hz is conventionally known as infrasound. Conventional sound level meters cannot measure infrasound.

The effect of infrasound is an area that has generated a lot of scientific argument; it is agreed that, as its intensity increases, it produces a general feeling of unease or discomfort rather than an identifiable aural effect. High intensities can produce resonances in discrete parts of the body including eyeballs, abdomen, chest and throat. Whole body exposure will produce general malaise and fatigue.

Infrasound is produced inside heavy vehicles and can reach 100 – 110dB in the range from 4 to 20 Hz. It is certainly a source of fatigue. However, surveys of lorry drivers' discomfort have shown noise to follow driving position as the most important factor, outweighing vibration, temperature, ventilation and visibility. Infrasound is also radiated by heavy machinery and large fans and ventilation systems. Large vibrating areas are usually needed to propagate low frequency sound efficiently; fixing a vibrating pipe to a large wall or panel provides it with an efficient sounding board.

Range Firing

The prediction of annoyance due to range firing or explosions is particularly difficult. To begin with, the sound level at a specific distance will depend on the source power, absorption effects due to the atmosphere and terrain en route, and on the local meteorological conditions. The effect of temperature gradients and wind on the ray paths is complicated and the best that is usually done is to restrict firing to favourable combinations of vector wind and temperature; see Chapter 2.

Except in the case of small arms, the annoyance arises mainly from vibrations within the building and from minor structural damage such as cracked windows or loose tiles. Given the response of buildings to low frequency sound, this is an area where the dB(A) is particularly inappropriate. The use of linear or 'C' weighting would be better.

There is at present no definite standard for maximum noise around civilian dwellings, although it has been suggested that peak pressure levels above 125 or 130 dB are likely to cause complaints. Obviously many other factors, including the frequency and timing of the noise, have to be considered. United States practice has tended towards use of the sound exposure level (SEL) — that is, the level which if maintained over 1 s period would have the same energy as the noise in question, but used with a 'C' weighting rather than the usual 'A' weighting.

Noise and Health

In general, it has been proved very difficult to demonstrate the existence of any long-term effects of noise on health except, of course, on hearing. Although some workers in noisy industries show an elevated incidence of sickness, it is not certain to what extent the effect is due to noise, and to what extent it is due to other aspects of the work. It is also difficult to provide a representative non-noise-exposed control group.

A number of short-term effects can be demonstrated. These include:

▶ Startle response.
▶ Changes in blood flow — vasoconstriction in peripheral regions, particularly in the skin.
▶ Increase in heart rate.

Small increases in blood pressure have frequently been reported, particularly in those with a family history of hypertension. Additionally, occasional rises in respiration rate have been reported. In general, no habituation in terms of physiological response has been reported on repeated exposure to noise.

The longer-term effects can be considered as a generalised stress response, seen as an increase in secretion of adrenal cortical hormones. There are many conditions which are widely considered to be associated with stress, although a direct relation between these conditions and noise exposure *per se* has not been proved. Detailed consideration of the stress response is beyond the scope of this book.

No firm conclusion is possible in this area at present; however, it appears that limits to noise exposure, set in respect of noise-induced hearing loss, should also protect against other effects on health.

Short exposures to very intense low-frequency noise, of sound pressure levels at and above 140 dB, have been shown to produce a variety of unpleasant but temporary symptoms.

11. Noise and Communication

Difficulties in Transmitting Intelligible Information

Adequate communication is essential in military activities. This chapter surveys the problems faced in understanding oral instructions in a noisy environment and in the use of a communications system intended to improve intelligibility. There are also occasions when non-communication is required, as in making a sound source undetectable to the enemy. The basic requirements for this are outlined.

With the increase in noise from military equipment, the effect of the noise on communication is becoming increasingly important. Apart from the reduction in efficiency due to orders being mis-heard, there will be an additional reduction since the effort required to understand speech transmitted by an unsatisfactory system will reduce the effort available for other tasks. To a large extent, the intelligibility of speech in a noisy environment can be predicted from measurements of the intensity, as a function of frequency, of both the speech and the noise. To see how this is done, we must first consider the nature of the speech signal.

Characteristics of Speech

Speech is a signal which varies rapidly in both intensity and frequency content. The lowest frequencies are generated by vibrations of the vocal cords in the larynx, when air is forced past them by the action of the lungs; frequencies generated in this way are unlikely to be far below 100 Hz, even for a deep voice. A number of harmonics are generated at the same time, and the way in which the intensity of these is modified by resonances in the throat and mouth gives much of the individual character of a voice.

The sounds generated by the vocal cords are mainly vowel sounds. Consonants are generated chiefly by the mouth and tongue, and consist mainly of higher frequencies, extending to about 6 kHz. The consonants carry most of the information in speech, although their intensity is less than that of the vowels.

Prediction of Intelligibility

The intelligibility of speech can to a large extent be predicted from the signal-to-noise ratio: that is, if the level of the speech signal comfortably exceeds the level of other noise, then the speech can be heard and understood. If the level of the noise is much greater than that of the speech, then the speech will not be understood. This calculation can be refined by using a number of bands covering the range of frequencies important in speech. The calculation is only valid if the listener has normal hearing.

Most of the intelligibility of speech is contained in the octave bands centred at 0.5, 1, 2 and 4 kHz, with a smaller contribution from the band centred at 250Hz. This information is used in the concept of the Speech Interference Level (SIL), which can be used to predict the intelligibility of unaided speech in noisy surroundings, such as a workshop. It is calculated as the mean of the octave band levels for the bands centred at 0.5, 1, 2 and 4 kHz. Where measurements in these bands are not available, the A-weighted sound level can be used as an approximate guide. As a rough approximation, a shouted message at a distance of 1 m may be understood if the SIL does not exceed 76 dB [equivalent to roughly 85 dB(A)]. A normal voice may be understood at 10 m if the SIL does not exceed 40 dB [equivalent to about 47 dB(A)). Fuller details are given in ANSI Standard S3.14 (1977).

Where an electronically amplified speech communication system is provided, an extension of this concept can be used. Here, however, we have to allow for distortion introduced by the system; the most serious distortion is generally the restricted range of frequencies transmitted by the system. For instance, if the frequency range is 300 Hz to 3 kHz, which is typical of many systems including ordinary telephones, then the intelligibility will generally be less than if a wider range, such as 200 Hz to 6 kHz, were used. However, the range 300 Hz to 3 kHz will normally be adequate, providing that no part of it is masked out by noise.

The Articulation Index uses the levels of both speech and noise within a number of bands to predict intelligibility. Octave bands can be used but greater precision is given by the use of one-third octave or narrower bands. The method is complex and the details are beyond the scope of this book. The concept is a very powerful one which can be used in many different situations; one weakness is that it cannot be used where speech is transmitted in coded form.

If the combined level of speech and noise at the ear reaches about 100 dB(A), then the intelligibility will be degraded by distortion generated within the overloaded ear. Such levels are very easily exceeded by intercommunications systems using headphones or other forms of headset with telephone transducers. This distortion becomes increasingly serious at higher levels, and at about 130 dB(A) is so bad that increasing the level of speech while keeping the noise constant gives no benefit. Such levels are, of course, accompanied by a very serious risk of noise-induced loss.

A more reliable indication of the quality of a communication system can be provided by direct measurement of the proportion of words or syllables heard correctly over the system. In general, single words or syllables having no special meaning should be used, as complete sentences or meaningful words are liable to be heard correctly under ideal test conditions even if the quality of the system in actual use is only marginal. The complete test is laborious and time-consuming, and of course gives little information on how the system should be improved.

Speech intelligibility can also be affected by other factors: an obvious example is a strong regional accent, which can be very difficult to understand for a person who does not come from that region. If either the speaker or listener is unfamiliar with the language used, then intelligibility will be reduced. In fact, there is some loss in intelligibility where the language is not the listener's native tongue, even if he can speak the language well enough to pass as a native speaker. On the other hand, intelligibility can be increased if the number of possible messages is limited, or where the message is couched in a deliberately restricted vocabulary. This is one reason for the stylised vocabulary used in radio procedure.

Redundant information in a message can help intelligibility. For instance, a single syllable is much more likely to be heard correctly if it forms an integral part of a sentence; the remainder of the sentence gives clues about what the syllable should be. Again, radio procedure gives a good example of this, in particular in its use of the phonetic alphabet where a whole word is used to indicate a single letter.

In general, if the intelligibility of the message is not good, the listener is apt to hear what he expects to hear. This can work well until an emergency arises, when it may be necessary to transmit a message which the listener does not expect.

A message is also less likely to be understood, or even heard at all, if the listener is already absorbed in a very important task, such as flying an aircraft in a difficult manoeuvre.

We see, then, that the quality needed in a communications system depends to some extent on the way the system is used. In particular , the content of the messages it is intended to transmit, the nature of other tasks performed by the listener and language barriers are important. Clearly, a system which is just adequate in some circumstances may prove seriously deficient in others.

Communications systems may be used for transmitting information other than speech; for instance, tones or other sounds may be used to signal engine malfunction. The audibility of such sounds can be predicted in a similar way to speech. It is very important to ensure that the meaning of sounds is consistent between systems. For instance, the alarm signal of one system should not resemble the sound indicating normal function of another system, especially if one operator is expected to use both! The number of possible signals should be as small as possible; ten is a practical limit for even highly trained specialist personnel, three or four is about all that can be employed in equipment designed for general use.

How to Improve a Communications System

In general, the strategy is to reduce the noise reaching the ear while keeping the bandwidth for speech as wide as possible. If we consider the common situation in very noisy environments, where communication is accomplished through some form of headset incorporating earphones and a microphone, we can see how these strategies can be employed. The best solution, as always, is to reduce the level of ambient noise; too often we are left with an unsatisfactory environment because noise was not sufficiently considered at the design stage.

The frequency response of an intercom system is generally limited to about 3 kHz, and even within this range is very uneven. There is a substantial potential benefit in increasing this to about 6 kHz. It is important to consider the response of the whole system, not just of individual components within it.

Noise enters the systems by one of three routes:

▶ Ambient acoustic noise penetrating a noise-excluding headset.

▶ Noise picked up by microphones and transmitted through the system.

▶ Radio and other interference.

Neglecting the third route, which is outside the scope of this book, we can find partial solutions to the other problems.

Noise-excluding Headset

The noise-excluding headset can generally be improved, since the passive attenuation which these devices give is rarely the best available. One example which springs to mind is a helmet originally procured as an 'interim' solution, still in service many years later, by which time its attenuation had fallen well behind the current state of the art. Note that the use of NBC-protective clothing and respirator will degrade the passive protection available; if the protection was poor to begin with, NBC equipment will reduce it almost to nothing.

Once a good passive attenuation has been secured, further improvements can be made where necessary by the use of an active system. In this system, a microphone placed near the ear produces a signal which is amplified, then subtracted from the noise using the telephone transducers in the headset. The use of the active system can reduce noise through the headset by about 10–12 dB.

Noise-cancelling Microphone

The noise picked up by the microphones can be reduced in several ways. Often a noise-cancelling microphone is used; this is placed very close to the lips and is more sensitive to nearby sources than to distant ones. Some microphones of this type are better than others, so some improvement is possible simply by using a better, more recently designed, microphone. Alternatively a mask microphone can be used. Throat microphones are insensitive to noise, but are not recommended; they pick up vibrations in the throat which, as we have seen, consist chiefly of vowel sounds with few consonants. They can also pick up mechanical vibration from vehicle movement.

Most users prefer permanently live microphones which can pick up speech without needing to be switched on. Unfortunately, this means that they also pick up noise at all times. One solution is the voice operated switch, which switches the microphone on when the level and frequency content corresponding to speech is detected. Earlier types were unpopular, due to their uncertain and intermittent operation and their tendency to clip the initial consonant of each sentence. More recent types largely avoid these problems.

Finally, if these measures are insufficient, it is possible to remove from the speech signal the frequencies most prominent in the noise. Much of the ambient noise usually consists of sharply defined and relatively constant tones, due for instance to engine firing or blade passage frequencies which change only slowly. It is possible for an adaptive noise cancelling system to track these frequencies and remove them from the speech signal: this has little effect on the speech which has a wide frequency range and components which change rapidly.

Reducing the noise in this way is important for hearing conservation as well as for intelligibility. It is quite possible, in noisy environments such as a tank, for noise at the ear beneath a headset to reach 110 dB(A) even without the speech signal. The speech has to be heard above this, and can easily increase the overall level by 6–12 dB(A). Live microphones can achieve nearly this increase even in the absence of speech.

Counter surveillance

It is often required that equipment be inaudible to enemy patrols passing within a stated distance. But what does 'inaudible' mean? If we assume that the noise must be below the threshold of normal hearing (very roughly, 0 dB in the range 1–6 kHz) then we run into a serious problem.

For example, assume that our equipment, which may be a generator, or slow moving vehicle, produces a level of 60 dB measured at a distance of 10 m. With spherical propagation and the inverse square law, the level at 100 m should then be 40 dB, since a 10-fold increase in distance gives a 20 dB reduction in level. At 1 km this would give 20 dB, neglecting, for the moment, atmospheric absorption and the effects of weather on propagation; and at 10 km, 0 dB — just audible.

Now there is clearly something wrong here since we know from experience that such equipment is usually not audible at 10 km. The factor omitted is the level of local background noise, which even under quiet rural conditions is generally sufficient to mask levels less than about 20 dB. Our equipment would then only be audible up to 1 km, and under noisy conditions only audible much closer. We are back to the problem of signal-to-noise ratio introduced earlier in the context of communication.

The only practical procedure is then to:

▶ Measure or estimate typical background noises at likely locations of the intruding patrols.

▶ Decide, inevitably somewhat arbitrarily, on the least noisy background likely in practice (for the worst case).

▶ Estimate the highest sound levels from our activities which will remain inaudible at the patrol's position.

It will be necessary, using the inverse square law, to convert the levels from the distance at which inaudibility is required to a convenient distance close to our equipment so that we can check by direct measurement that it is not producing too high a level there.

The alert reader will have spotted many assumptions in all this:

▶ First, the detectability of a sound is not just a matter of the level in dB(A) increasing by a certain amount. We cannot put a single figure on it since the detectability in fact depends on the frequency contents of both the sound and the background, and on the complex way in which the brain recognises some sounds as particularly significant even in a noisy environment. We can get a better idea by analysing noise in one-third octave bands; if the sound from the equipment exceeds the background noise in any band, the equipment may be heard. Whether it will be heard depends on, amongst other things, the alertness and training of the listener.

Sound levels thus need to be specified in octave or one-third octave bands, possibly with levels in dB(A) as a rough approximation. This approach is taken by some standards, notably US MIL-STD-1474B.

▶ Secondly, the sound from the source will have suffered an energy loss en route due to the atmospheric absorption briefly mentioned in Chapter 2. This loss will depend on frequency and the relative humidity of the air. Putting precise figures on the effect is difficult with atmospheric variables that may change with time and place.

Approximate working figures, in terms of the resulting reduction in decibels per km of range, are included in Table 11.1.

TABLE 11.1 ATMOSPHERIC ABSORPTION COEFFICIENTS

Frequency (Hz)	63	125	250	500	1000	2000	4000	8000
Absorption loss (dB/km)	0.1	0.3	1.0	2.5	4.5	9.0	25.0	88.0

It is easy to see that the practical significance of these losses, when compared with the reduction due to spreading, depends markedly on range and frequency. For example, the reduction at 250 Hz from 1 km range to 2 km will be 6 dB due to spreading and 1.0 db due to absorption; going from 1 km to 4 km range, however, involves a 12 dB reduction due to spreading, as there are two doublings of distance, and (3 x 1.0) or 3 dB due to absorption. At this low frequency, the absorption loss remains less than the spreading effect up to about 8 km range. The situation becomes quite different at higher frequencies. Recalculating the data at 4000 Hz shows the absorption loss from 1 to 2 km to be 25 dB and from 1 to 4 km it is (3 x 25) or 75 dB!

There is another factor that affects the sound level at a distant point when the source and receiver are close to the ground. We then have the situation shown in Figure. 2.11 with direct and reflected waves. How much energy is reflected will on the nature of the ground surface. If it is a hard rigid surface, such as concrete, reflection will be high. On the other hand, a soil surface made porous by the root systems of covering vegetation will reflect less well. With grassland there can be a significant reduction in level in the frequency range of 250–500 Hz. The actual value depends on range and the angle of incidence on the ground of the sound; for optimum concealment a source needs to be very close to the ground.

Vegetation and trees might also be expected to scatter the sound by providing a series of small barriers. Recalling the point made in Chapter 2, however, there will be little effect unless the wavelength of the sound is comparable to or less than the dimensions of the obstacle. For foliage, there is consequently little effect below 500 Hz, even with thick belts of woodland. At 4000 Hz a 50 m thick, dense belt is needed to provide about 12 dB reduction. In practical terms it may be prudent to ignore this effect of foliage, unless high frequencies are dominant.

Since both background noise and atmospheric propagation vary, it is never possible to guarantee that equipment will always be inaudible at a stated distance, but it should be possible to guarantee that it will be inaudible on most occasions. If the sources are too noisy for inaudibility at the required range, there are only two choices — increase the minimum distance of approach or to reduce noise emission, for instance by adding a portable insulating unit around the source. Figure 8.11 showed a simple example used to quieten a Honda generator.

Summary

Speech intelligibility in a noisy environment depends on the intensity and frequency range of the ambient noise as well as on the intensity and frequency content of the spoken message. Noise reaching the ear may be reduced by a noise excluding headset or by noise reducing microphones but there are limitations in their performance. In particular the practice of using permanently live microphones can produce high noise levels in the ear for long durations.

The same idea of signal-to-noise ratio is involved in detecting militarily significant sounds outdoors. A simplified prediction scheme to calculate the maximum sound level near the source giving inaudibility at a required range is used to illustrate the principles involved.

12. Unit Hearing Conservation Programmes

Previous chapters in this book have revealed the many sources of potential hazard to hearing that are present in military environments. Various methods have also been suggested for reducing the risk of noise-induced hearing loss. The principal solutions are:

▶ Reducing the noise at source.

▶ Isolating the noise source, for instance by sound insulation.

▶ Monitoring the noise exposure and reducing the exposure time when appropriate.

▶ Instituting an audiometric programme.

▶ Educating workforce and management.

▶ Where the above are by themselves insufficient; providing, and ensuring the use of, hearing protection.

To put these ideas into practice requires the continual monitoring of noise levels and of personnel at risk, to ensure that the precautionary measures taken are proving effective. The organisation of this is provided by a Hearing Conservation Programme, ideally having the following features.

Features of a Unit Hearing Conservation Programme

▶ Appointment of a 'nominated individual' (or Hearing Conservation Officer) to act as a focus for hearing conservation measures.

▶ Identification of hazardous areas, and the reduction or isolation, as far as possible, of problem noise sources.

▶ Audiometry of personnel at risk (in a Service environment, this effectively means audiometry of all personnel).

▶ Provision and maintenance of hearing protection where necessary.

▶ Education of the workforce.

Appointment of a 'Nominated' Individual

This individual may, or may not, be a unit safety officer. In any event it is essential that he or she should be in continuous contact with the working areas concerned and be aware of the importance of his/her responsibility for the future well-being of the workforce. This requires the active backing of management. The monitoring task must be done on a continuous basis and not reduced to the periodic inspection familiar in Service life which provides a highly artificial impression of working conditions.

It is essential that nominated individuals are adequately educated in the various aspects of the problems dealt with in this book. One method proving very successful is the (United Kingdom) RAF procedure of requiring unit Hearing Conservation Officers to attend a 2-day course specifically designed for their needs. Realistically, it must be acknowledged that this task of monitoring noise hazards may be yet another secondary duty given to an already busy individual. Any course of instruction must clearly be of obvious relevance to his needs, with an emphasis on actual examples drawn from the relevant area of operation and given by people who are very familiar with the real day-to-day working environment at unit level. Again the assistance of higher management is needed to make such courses available, and known to be available, and attendance on them encouraged. It is hoped that this book will have made a contribution to the training of higher management itself in the need to take noise hazards more seriously than in the past. The possibility of personnel taking legal action against Service employers should prove an incentive.

Identification of Hazardous Areas or Tasks

The nominated individual needs assistance in his task by the provision of simple equipment to identify noise hazardous areas. This, at least, requires a simple dB(A) meter and calibrator, although the operator must be aware of the limitations of such equipment e.g. in dealing with fluctuating noise or noise with an impulsive content. Chapters 5 and 7 have given more detailed guidance. Where more detailed noise surveys are required, back-up teams with more specialised equipment and experience should be available via a clearly identified procedure.

There are easily identifiable duties in the Services which are particularly hazardous. Such special risk duties include weapons instructors, tracked vehicle driving instructors, men exposed to a significant amount of weapon noise or long periods within vehicles known to be particularly noisy, aircrew, groundcrew involved in marshalling, refuelling or rearming aircraft or providing pre-flight checks at high engine power, and personnel in ship's engine rooms.

Audiometry of Personnel at Risk

In large organisations such as the Services, it is essential that medical staff responsible for audiometric monitoring should be provided with up-to-date lists of personnel working in hazardous noise environments. Nominated individuals in close contact with the workforce are best placed to provide these. Conversely, medical staff should advise nominated individuals of significant threshold shifts among their charges, as this could indicate the presence of an undetected hazardous area or working operation. There is thus a need for a satisfactory working relationship between the nominated individual and the relevant medical staff; this is not always the case.

The requirements for satisfactory audiometry have been discussed in detail in Chapter 4. It should be mandatory that base-line audiograms are taken when an individual joins a Service and regularly (ideally, annually) after that. More frequent checks would be useful for any personnel identified as being particularly at risk. Medical records which maintain a complete audiometric history of an individual are essential, a task not made easier by frequent postings. Personnel not keeping audiometric appointments need to be pursued.

Each audiogram must be compared with previous ones. There is no point in audiograms being routinely filed away in an individual's records without any attempt to identify threshold shifts and to take further action. Audiograms with changes in hearing threshold should be shown to the person involved so that he or she can see evidence of a deterioration before it becomes subjectively evident; this should bring home the importance of the Hearing Conservation Programme.

Provision of Hearing Protection

Personnel exposed to noise levels exceeding 85 dB(A) should be provided with suitable hearing protection and encouraged to wear it. The provision of hearing protection at and above an L_{eq} of 85 dB(A) will be required by forthcoming legislation.

The suitability of particular forms of hearing protection has been examined in Chapter 9. The nominated individual has the vital task of ensuring that suitable protection is available, that the workforce actually wear it and are aware of how to fit it and how to care for it, and of the possible consequences of not so doing. This implies that the nominated individual has facilities and time available for educating personnel.

Education of the Workforce

An educational programme for personnel has the aim of involving them in the Hearing Conservation Programme and producing self-discipline in their attitude to noise. The main points to be included in any training course include:

▶ The effect of noise on hearing, threshold shifts, the significance of audiometry, the irreversible destruction of the hearing mechanism and the time delay before these effects become noticeable. The possible effect of hearing loss on future employment/promotion within the Service.

▶ Causes of noise-induced hearing loss, local sources providing a hazard, noise dose combining dB(A) and time, contribution of on-and off-duty noise, recognition of hazardous areas by need to shout at 1m range.

▶ The necessary use of hearing protection at sound pressure levels above 85 dB(A); precautions in using protectors, where to obtain them or replacements. Possible disciplinary action if protection is not worn. Demonstration that wearing protection does not reduce the ability to perform a task.

Relevant video-cassettes are available from Service organisations and industry. Three good examples in the United Kingdom available from Services Sound and Vision Corporation are 'The Noise was Deafening', 'Dangerous Noise, Part 1' and 'Listen'. Demonstration material is usually available from the manufacturers of hearing protection.

Answers to Self Test Questions

Chapter 2

Question 1 From $v = f\lambda$, $\lambda = \dfrac{v}{f}$ where $v = 330$ m s^{-1}.

For $f = 300$ Hz, $\lambda = \dfrac{330}{300} = 1.1$ m; for $f = 3000$ Hz, $\lambda = \dfrac{330}{3000} = 0.11$ m

Question 2 Energy from the voice is small. Much of this is reflected by, or spreads round, the kettle.

Question 3 An earth bank is only useful if its height is a few times greater than the sound wavelengths involved. The 1257 Hz would be easier since wavelength is only about $330/1257 = 0.26$ m. For the 19 Hz sound, the wavelength is $330/19 = 17.4$ m!

Question 4 Shadow will cease to be sharp when spreading takes place, which requires the head diameter to become about 1 wavelength in size. Typical the head is about 18 cm between the ears, hence the critical frequency would be about $330/0.18 = 1830$ Hz.

Question 5 Intensity = power emitted (watts)/(area over which energy is spread). Here the area is of a sphere of radius 10 m and

$$I = \dfrac{100}{4\pi(10^2)} = 0.08 \text{ W m}^{-2}.$$

Chapter 3

Question 1 (a) We use the pressure definition of the dB, $20 \log \dfrac{p}{p_0}$.

Hence $20 \log_{10} \dfrac{16}{2 \times 10^{-5}} = 20 \log (8 \times 10^5) = 20 \times 5.9 = 118$ dB.

(b) No. The A-weighted sound level would give a better indication.

Question 2 We have to calculate the two respective intensities I involved, add them, and find the resulting level in dB.

For 90 dB, $90 = 10 \log \dfrac{I}{10^{-12}}$ giving $10^9 = \dfrac{I}{10^{-12}}$ and $I = 10^{-3}$ W m^{-2}.

For 95 dB, $95 = 10 \log \dfrac{I}{10^{-12}}$ giving $I = 3.16 \times 10^{-3}$ W m^{-2}.

Total intensity is $(1 + 3.16) \times 10^{-3} = 4.16 \times 10^{-3}$ W m^{-2}.

Back into dB form, we get $10 \log \dfrac{4.16 \times 10^{-3}}{10^{-12}} = 96.2$ dB.

For the nomogram, the difference in our two levels is 5 dB and we enter it from below at this 5 dB difference. Reading upwards we have to add 1.2 dB to the higher level, giving 96.2 dB.

Question 3 The large drop to the dB(A) value means a lot of low frequencies are present. A 30 dB drop suggests 63 Hz as the dominant frequency range (see Table 3.2).

Question 4 Neglecting all contributions below 90 dB, as the maximum band level is 100 dB, we pair as follows:

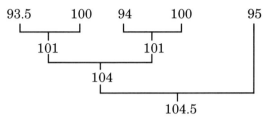

The overall level is 104.5 dB, corresponding to the value actually measured of 104 dB.

Question 5 Using the conversions in the text we get the following:

Frequency (Hz):   31.5   63   125   250   500 1000 2000 4000 8000
Levels in dB(A):   51   76   86   92   93   91   86   84   69

To add these, we can neglect those 10 dB(A) or more below the highest (at 31.5, 63 and 8000 Hz). Taking the following pairs and using the nomogram of Figure. 3.3:

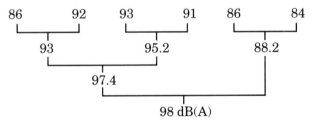

giving a total of 98 dB(A).

Question 6 Using the conversions in the text we get the following:

Frequency (Hz):   63   125   250   500   1000   2000   4000   8000
In Front   50   69   81   88   95 105.5 105.5   105
At 135°:   65   79   90   96   95   98.5   93.5   88

In front, we only need to combine 95 dB(A) and upwards, giving a total of 110 dB(A) using the nomogram. At 135°, we add levels above 88 dB(A):

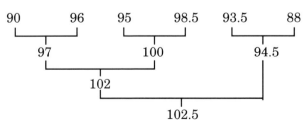

giving a total of 102.5 dB(A).

The sound directly in front of the aircraft is dominated by the high frequency whine of the compressor and turbine. Round towards the rear, the exhaust roar produces more energy at the lower frequencies.

Chapter 6

Question 1 Level-duration combinations are: 85/8 h, 88/4 h, 91/2 h, 94/1 h, 97/30 min, 100/15 min, 103/7½ min.

Checking by the procedure in the text,
1. $7½/480 = 0.0156$,
2. $10 \log 0.0156 = -18.0$,
3. $103 + (-18) = 85 \text{dB(A)}$.

Question 2 We now work backwards through the steps.
3. $110 + x = 85 \text{ dB(A)}$ gives the correction x.
   $x = 85 - 110 = -25$.
2. $10 \log y = -25$ where y is the fractional time exposure.
   $y = \text{antilog } -2.5 = 0.00316$.
1. $t/480 = 0.00316$ so that the exposure time t is $0.00316 \times 480 = 1.5$ min.

Question 3 By the procedure in the text, for the 104 dB(A) exposures, lasting a total of 30 min.
1. $30/480 = 0.0625$,
2. $10 \log 0.0625 = -12.0$,
3. $104 + (-12) = 92 \text{ dB(A)}$.

The 7½ h at 85 dB(A) gives:
2. $10 \log 7½/8 = -0.03$,
3. $75 + (-0.03) = 75 \text{ dB(A)}$, negligible compared with the first contribution.

The $L_{eq(8)}$ is therefore 92 dB(A).

Question 4 By the same procedure, respective contributions to L_{eq} are 87 and 92 dB(A), adding to 93 dB(A).

Question 5 His actual exposure pattern was 111 dB(A) for 2 min, 93 dB(A) for 3 min and 100 dB(A) for 5 min. Returning to the procedure of Chapter 6:
1. For 111 dB(A) and 2 min, $10 \log 2/480 = -23.8$ and
$$L_{eq(8)} = 111 + (-24) = 87 \text{ dB(A)}.$$

2. For 93 dB(A) and 3 min, $10 \log 3/480 = -22$ and
$$L_{eq(8)} = 93 + (-22) = 71 \text{ dB(A)}.$$

3. For 100 dB(A) and 5 min, $10 \log 5/480 = -19.8$ and
$$L_{eq(8)} = 100 + (-20) = 80 \text{ dB(A)}.$$

These add to 88 dB(A), above a daily allowed RAF dose. He needs to read Chapter 9 on the correct use of hearing protection.

It would not help significantly if he moved away from the GPU since the 111 dB(A) exposure near the aircraft dominates the total noise dose. The procedure of Question 2 above, however, shows that he would only need to remain by the GPU for 15 min to achieve an 85 dB(A) equivalent there. It would be wise to wear hearing protection all the time.

Chapter 7

Question 1 8 kPa in dB terms is $20 \log \dfrac{8000}{2 \times 10^{-5}} = 172$ dB. For a *single* round we can add 10 dB (Figure 7.10) to the criteria of Figure 7.9. At a duration of 3 ms the maximum allowed dB is 170 dB. Hence no single unprotected firings are allowed.

Question 2 (a) From Figure 7.9, maximum peak pressure for 100 rounds per day of 20 ms duration is 155 dB. For only 10 rounds per day, add allowance of 5 dB from Figure 7.9, making 160 dB allowed. If the hearing protection is assumed to give 20 dB effective protection, then 180 dB would be permissible. Hence exposure is just allowed.

(b) No. If very effective hearing protection was used, giving a 25 dB effective protection, one round could be fired in 24 h, but this is hardly practical.

Question 3 (a) Outdoors, no problem.

(b) Above the maximum limit, even for one round, unless hearing protection is used.

Chapter 8

Question 1 Following on from text, $10 \log \dfrac{I/4}{I} = 10 \log \frac{1}{4} = -6$ dB.

Question 2 (a) Terms explained in Glossary and text.

(b) If intensity depends on 1/(total absorption), then doubling the total absorption will halve the intensity. Comparing the two intensities, $10 \log \dfrac{I/2}{I} = 10 \log \frac{1}{2} = -3$ dB.

Question 3 (a) With door shut, insulation difference is 33dB and ratio of areas is 1:20. From Figure 8.8 the better insulator loses about 20 dB to become 55-20 = 35 dB.

(b) Door open means the door insulation is now zero, the difference in insulations becomes 55, but the area ratio is still 1:20. From Figure 8.8 the better insulation now loses about 42 dB to become 55-42 = 13 dB.

Question 4 Data in the table give, using the nomogram of Figure 3.3, total levels of 111dB with the door open and 103 dB with the door shut. Since the dominant frequencies are mainly in the low kHz region we expect the dB(A) levels to be not far off the dB levels. Using the conversions of Table 3.2 and the nomogram we find totals of 110 dB(A) with the door open and 101 dB(A) for the door shut.

On the RAF criterion of 85 dB(A) for $L_{eq(8)}$, these levels are allowed for 1.5 min and 12 min respectively in a day. The door needs to be bricked up!

Chapter 9

Question 1

Frequency(Hz)	63	125	250	500	1000	2000	4000	8000
Level dB	110	124	120	111	106	94	83	93
Plug has assumed protection (mean — 1 sd) in dB:								
dB	18	18	20	22	24	28	39	38
Subtracting these from source levels gives at the ear (dB):								
dB	92	106	100	89	82	66	44	55
Reduce to 'A' weighted levels by adding corrections:								
dB	−26	−16	−9	−3	0	1	1	−1
giving 'A' weighted levels at the ear:								
dB(A)	66	90	91	86	82	67	45	54
These add to 94.5 dB(A).								

The plug reduces the level at the ear from 115 to 95 dB(A). This would be allowable for about 2½ h.

Question 2

Frequency	63	125	250	500	1000	2000	4000	8000
dB	107	112	114	119	123	121	116	105
Muff had assumed protection of:								
dB	12	8	13	21	31	32	35	27
Hence dB levels reaching the ear are:								
dB	95	104	101	98	92	89	81	78
Reduce to 'A' weighted levels by adding corrections:								
dB	−26	−16	−9	−3	0	1	1	−1
to give 'A' weighted levels at the ear:								
dB(A)	69	88	92	95	92	90	82	77
These add to 99 dB(A).								
The original noise levels before hearing protection, converted to dB(A) are:								
dB(A)	81	96	105	116	123	122	117	104
which add up to 127 dB(A).								

Notice that here the muff provides an effective reduction of 28 dB(A), whereas the same muff in the text calculation for the tracked vehicle yielded only 13 dB(A). This is because of its poor performance at low frequencies, more significant in the latter case. This is a good example of different protector types being more suitable for a given source characteristic.

Glossary of Technical Terms

N.B. These are explanations of the terms and not formal definitions. The latter are included in BS 4727, Part 3, Group 08 (1985).

A

'A' Weighting
> Used with noise measuring equipment to give approximately the same response to different frequencies as the human ear.

Absorption coefficient
> Fraction of incident acoustic energy absorbed by a surface.

Acoustic trauma
> Hearing damage due to a single exposure to intense noise, e.g. a thunderflash.

Active noise reduction
> Reduction of noise by combining the sound with a version of itself which is 180° out of phase.

Attenuation
> A reduction in sound level. The concept is used in sound insulation and hearing protection.

Audibility threshold (threshold of hearing)
> Sound pressure level at a particular frequency which is just audible to personnel with normal hearing.

Audiometer
> Instrument for measuring the threshold of hearing; more complex types of audiometer will give additional measures of hearing function.

Aural (acoustic) reflex
> Muscle system which reacts to loud sounds by restraining movement of bones in middle ear.

B

Band sound pressure level
> Sound pressure level within a specified frequency band.

Bandwidth
> The range of frequencies effectively passed by a filter.

Basilar membrane
> Region of inner ear bearing hair (nerve) cells which responds to incoming vibrations from sound to produce signals to brain.

C

'C' Weighting
> Used with noise measuring equipment to reduce sensitivity to very high and very low frequencies in a well-defined manner.

Centre frequency (of an octave or one-third octave band filter)
> The geometric mean $\sqrt{f_1 f_2}$ of the highest and lowest frequencies, f_1 and f_2, within a band.

D

dB(A)
> Sound pressure level measured using an 'A' weighting.

dB(C)
> Sound pressure level measured using a 'C' weighting.

Decibel scale
> A scale of measurement involving taking 10 times the logarithm (to base 10) of a measured energy ratio. See Chapter 3 for a full explanation.

Diffraction
> The spreading of sound through an aperture, or round an object, of size comparable to, or smaller than, one wavelength.

Direct sound
> Sound reaching the ear straight from the source and not from a wall reflection, etc.

E

Ear defender
> Another name for a hearing protector.

Effective protection (of a hearing protector)
> At a particular frequency, the mean attenuation minus the standard deviation. Eighty-three per cent of users will obtain more attenuation than this — if the protector is correctly used!

Equivalent continuous sound level
> The constant sound level that would have the same total energy over the measurement period as the actual fluctuating sound. The use of an 'A' weighting is assumed unless otherwise specified, and the result is then expressed in dB(A). The usual abbreviation is L_{eq}. It is written as $L_{eq(8)}$ or $L_{EP,d}$ if the measurement period is the conventional 8 h.

F

Free field
> A region free of reflecting surfaces. Rare, with the ground at least usually present.

Frequency
> The number of cycles of the sound wave in one second. Unit: hertz (Hz).

Frequency spectrum
> The distribution of sound energy as a function of frequency. Usually measured as octave or one-third octave band sound pressure levels. Must be known when attempting to quieten a sound source or when assessing the effectiveness of hearing protection.

H

Hearing conservation
> An integrated approach to the reduction of noise-induced hearing loss. It includes the reduction of noise at source, the isolation of noise sources, the reduction of exposure time, the monitoring of noise exposure, monitoring audiometry, education and (where necessary) the provision and maintenance of hearing protectors.

Hearing level
>An individual's threshold of hearing compared with 'normal' values.

Hearing loss
>The rise in the audibility threshold due to age, injury, disease or noise.

Hearing protector
>Ear plug, ear muff or noise-excluding helmet worn to reduce the noise reaching the ear.

I

Impulse noise
>Noise of short duration and high peak pressure, for instance noise from weapons. It requires specialist measurement techniques.

Infrasound
>Sound of frequency below the normal audible range (nominally 20 Hz).

Intensity
>The amount of acoustic energy crossing one square metre per second. It falls off with distance from a source as the energy is spread over increasing area and is related to the square of the acoustic pressure.

L

Loudness
>Subjective impression of the intensity of a sound. It depends on frequency and is roughly measured by the 'A' weighted sound pressure level.

M

Masking
>Process by which the threshold of audibility of one sound is raised by the presence of another (masking) sound. It is most apparent when sounds are in the same frequency range, as the same region of the basilar membrane is involved.

N

Near field
>The complicated region near a source where waves from different parts of the source have travelled different distances to the measuring point and may interfere with one another (reinforce or cancel).

Noise dose meter
>An electronic device to give a direct read-out of the noise dose by integrating the 'A' weighted sound pressure level over the measurement duration.

O

Octave
>Two pure tones are one octave apart if the frequency of one is twice the frequency of the other.

Octave band
>A range of frequencies such that the highest frequency is twice the lowest frequency.

Octave band centre frequency
>The geometric mean of the highest and lowest frequencies within an

octave band. The conventional centre frequencies are:
31.5, 63, 125, 250, 500, 1000, 2000, 4000, 8000 and 16,000 Hz.

Octave band filter

An electronic filter which will pass sound at all frequencies within an octave band, and reject sound at other frequencies.

One-third octave band filter

Splits each octave band into three, to give more detail than octave band filters.

P

Pascal (abbreviation: Pa)

Unit of pressure, being 1 newton per square metre ($1 \, N \, m^{-2}$). 1 pound per square inch is approximately 6895 pascal.

Normal atmospheric pressure is about 100,000 Pa (100 kPa).

Peak pressure (or peak sound pressure)

Maximum departure (positive or negative) of instantaneous pressure from ambient (atmospheric) pressure.

R

Reference sound pressure

Used in the definition of sound pressure level; has a value of 2×10^{-5} Pa ($20 \, \mu Pa$).

Resonance

An enhanced reaction of a mechanical system to sound in a narrow frequency band.

Reverberation

The persistence of sound after the source has stopped. It is due to sound bouncing off walls, etc. Can be the dominant source of sound at a large distance from the source and may be reduced by increasing absorption.

Root-mean-square (rms)

The square root of the arithmetic average of a set of squared values. For a sine wave, $p_{rms} = 0.71 \times p_{peak}$.

S

Sound exposure level

The continuous sound pressure level over a 1–second period which has the same energy as the sound being measured. The use of an 'A' weighting is assumed unless otherwise specified.

Sound pressure level (measured in dB)

$20 \log p/p_0$ where p is the measured rms pressure and p_0 the reference value of 2×10^{-5} Pa.

Sound reduction index (SRI) [or transmission loss (TL)]

Reduction of sound pressure level across a wall or barrier.

Speech interference level (SIL)

Arithmetic average of octave band sound pressure levels in the 500, 1000, 2000 and 4000 Hz octave bands.

Standard deviation (sd)

A statistical quantity which reveals the spread in data. Sixty-seven per cent of normally distributed data will be within ± one standard deviation of the mean value. Important in the concept of effective protection provided by hearing protectors.

T

Threshold of hearing (audibility threshold)

Sound pressure level at a particular frequency which is just audible to personnel with 'normal' hearing.

Threshold shift (TS)

A change in the threshold of hearing, usually an increase, which indicates that hearing has become worse. In our context, it is usually due to noise exposure. May be temporary (TTS) or permanent (PTS). It may also be due to ageing (presbycusis) or disease.

Tinnitus

Apparent high pitched whistle or 'ringing' in the ear. Severe tinnitus is usually associated with ear injury or disease.

Total absorption

The sum of all the surface areas in a workshop multiplied by their respective absorption coefficients.

Transmission loss (TL)

See 'sound reduction index'.

U

Ultrasound

Sound of frequency above the normal audible range (nominally 20,000 Hz).

W

Wavelength (λ)

The distance in space before a wave starts to repeat its shape.

Selected Bibliography

General Aspects of Noise

BRUEL and KJAER Ltd, Harrow, Middlesex. *Acoustic Noise Measurements*, 1979; and *Noise Control*, 1986; two of a series of excellent booklets written for non-specialists.

BURNS, W. *Noise and Man*, 2nd Edn. John Murray, London, 1973.

HARRIS, C.M. (Ed.) *Handbook of Noise Control*, 2nd Edn. McGraw-Hill, New York, 1979. This book includes, among other topics, survey articles by Burns on *'Physiological Effects of Noise'*, by Broadbent on *'Noise and Behaviour'* and by Tonndorf, von Gierke and Ward, on *'Criteria for Noise and Vibration Exposure'*. Articles on standards for noise tend to reflect American rather than British practice.

HEALTH AND SAFETY EXECUTIVE (UK), *100 Practical Applications of Noise Reduction Methods'*, HMSO, London, 1983.

KRYTER, K.D. *The Effects of Noise on Man*, 2nd Edn. Academic Press, London, 1985. A very comprehensive textbook with a wealth of references to research work in this field. A book for serious study.

LARA SAENZ, A. and STEPHENS, R.W.B. (Eds) *Noise Pollution*, John Wiley, Chichester, 1986.

LORD, H., GATLEY, W.S. and EVENSEN, H.A. *Noise Control for Engineers*, McGraw-Hill, New York, 1980. A comprehensive text with a practical emphasis. American noise criteria are used.

TEMPEST, W. (Ed.) *The Noise Handbook*, Academic Press, London, 1985. A very useful survey of the whole field, including current legal aspects and likely future changes in noise limits following EEC directives.

Impulse Noise

In contrast to the vast amount of published material on other aspects of acoustics, there are comparatively few general publications on impulse noise. However, a review of current knowledge and research work, together with specific recommendations on impulse noise measurements, is given in the following publications:

BAKER, W.E. *Explosions in Air*, University of Texas Press, Austin and London, 1973. Gives a detailed description of impulse noise and blast.

FARRAR, C.L. and LEEMING, D.W. *'Military Ballistics: A Basic Manual'*, Battlefield Weapons Systems and Technology, Volume X, Brassey's Publishers Ltd, (1983) (uniform with this volume). An excellent introductory textbook on ballistics, which includes a description of the mechanism of impulse noise generation from weapons in the chapter on Intermediate Ballistics.

NATO DEFENCE RESEARCH GROUP, Panel 8 (Human Factors), Research Study Group 6 on Effects of Impulse Noise, 1986. Final Report *'Effects of Impulse Noise'*.

National and International Standards

American National Standard for Rating Noise with Respect to Speech Interference, ANSI S3.14, 1977.

British Standards Institution, 1961. Normal equal-loudness contours for pure tones and normal thresholds of hearing under free-field listening conditions. *BS 3383:1961.* (Technically equivalent to ISO R226.)

British Standards Institution, 1967. Method of rating industrial noise affecting mixed residential and industrial areas. *BS 4142:1967 (amended 1982).*

British Standards Institution, 1976. Method of test for estimating the risk of hearing handicap due to noise exposure. *BS 5330:1976.* (Similar to, although *not* identical with, ISO 1999.)

British Standards Institution, 1981. Specification for sound level meters. *BS 5969:1981.* (Identical with IEC 651-1979.)

British Standards Institution, 1983. Measurement of sound attenuation of hearing protectors. *BS 5108:1983.* (Identical with ISO 4869-1981).

British Standards Institution, 1984. Industrial hearing protectors: Part 1 — Specification for ear muffs. *BS 6344:Part 1 (revised).* (An International Standard on this topic is in preparation.)

British Standards Institution, 1985. British Standard glossary of electrotechnical, power, telecommunication, electronics, lighting and colour terms: Part 3 — Terms peculiar to telecommunications and electronics. Group 08. Acoustics and electroacoustics terminology. *BS 4727:Part 3:Group 08:1985.*

Council of the European Communities, 1986. Council Directive of 12 May 1986 on the protection of workers from the risks related to exposure to noise at work. *Official Journal of the European Communities,* No. L 137/28 to L 137/34 of 12 May 1986. Although not a standard in the strict sense of the term, this Directive will form the basis for legislation to be introduced by individual nations within the European Community.

Military Standards

Department of Defense, USA. Military Standard. *Noise Limits for Army Materiel, MIL-STD-1474B (M1), 1979.* (Includes specifications for both impulse and continuous noise.)

Ministry of Defence, Directorate of Standardization, 1985. Acceptable limits for exposure to impulse noise from military weapons, explosives and pyrotechnics. *Defence Standard 00-27 / Issue 1, 16 July 1985.*

NATO Military Agency for Standardization. Guidelines governing noise levels in ships. *Standardization Agreement (STANAG) 1186.*

NATO Military Agency for Standardization. Protection of Hearing. *Standardization Agreement (STANAG) 2899.* (Concerned with hearing conservation practice.)

Index